Investigating Earth Science

Dusty Girard
Rick Lynn

Kendall Hunt
publishing company

Kendall Hunt
publishing company

www.kendallhunt.com
Send all inquiries to:
4050 Westmark Drive
Dubuque, IA 52004-1840

Copyright © 2017 by Kendall Hunt Publishing Company

ISBN 978-1-5249-2171-2

Published in the United States of America

Contents

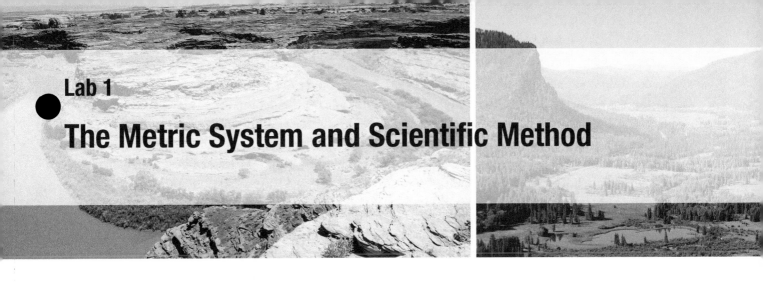

Lab 1

The Metric System and Scientific Method

Length, Volume, and Mass

The metric system is a decimal based system. It uses a single base unit for each type of measurement. The meter (m) is used for length, the liter (l) is a measurement of volume, the gram (g) is the unit of mass, and temperature is measured on the Celsius (C) scale. Similar units in the English system are feet, quarts, and ounces. In the English system, temperature is measured on the Fahrenheit (F) scale.

The basic units in the metric system are scaled up or down by factors of ten to create new units. This is similar to our monetary system where ten pennies equals a dime and ten dimes equal a dollar. Table 1.1 shows prefixes which are used to modify the base units.

The advantage of the metric system is ease of conversion. Since everything is specified in units of ten, measurements are easily converted from one unit to another just by moving a decimal point. For example, 3,000 meters (m) is 3 kilometers (km). By moving the decimal point to the left three places, we converted from meters to kilometers. To convert from meters to centimeters, move the decimal point to the right two places. For example, 3,000 m becomes 300,000 cm. Another way to perform this conversion is to multiply or divide by a power of ten. When moving from a larger to a smaller scale (i.e. from kilo to deka) one must multiply by a factor of ten (move the decimal point

Table 1.1 Prefixes used with the base units of the metric system. Some prefixes are rarely used such as hecto and deka.

giga	G	base unit times 1 billion	(base * 1,000,000,000)
mega	M	base unit times 1 million	(base * 1,000,000)
kilo	k	base unit times 1 thousand	(base * 1,000)
hecto	h	base unit times 1 hundred	(base * 100)
deka	da	base unit times 10	(base * 10)
base unit (meters, liters, grams)			
deci	d	base unit times 1/10	(base * .1)
centi	c	base unit times 1/100	(base * .01)
milli	m	base unit times 1/1,000	(base * .001)
micro	μ	base unit times 1/1,000,000	(base * .000001)
nano	n	base unit times 1/1,000,000,000	(base * .000000001)

to the right one place for each factor of ten). Moving from a smaller to a larger scale (i.e. from centi to the base unit) one must divide by a factor of ten (move the decimal point to the left one place for each factor of ten). For example, to determine the number of kilometers represented by 2,500 meters, divide meters by 1,000 therefore (2,500 m / 1,000)=2.5 km. Because we moved from a smaller (the base unit) to a larger scale (kilo) we divided by 1,000. To determine how many centimeters are in 2,500 m, we must multiply by 100 so (2,500 m *100)=250,000 cm. To convert 2 km to centimeters, we would have to multiply by 100,000. The result is (2 km*100,000)=200,000 cm.

If you are still confused, think of the metric system like the units we use for money. A dollar is the base unit for our monetary system. A penny (one cent) is a centidollar because it is 1/100 of a dollar or a dime would be a decidollar because it is 1/10 of a dollar. One thousand dollars would be a kilodollar and $1,000,000 would be a megadollar.

Another advantage of the metric system is the fact that units can be easily interchanged. For example, 1 milliliter (ml, a measurement of volume) is the same as 1 cubic centimeter (cm). So we have converted from a measure of volume to a measure of length. Also, 1 gram (a measure of mass) is equal to 1 milliliter therefore 1 gram is also equal to 1 cubic centimeter. Such conversions in the English system are much more difficult. For example, to convert from gallons to cubic feet you must multiply gallons by .13368!

Temperature

Using the Fahrenheit scale to measure temperature, water freezes at 32°F and boils at 212°F. On the Celsius scale water freezes at 0° and boils at 100°c.
To convert from Celsius (C) to Fahrenheit (F):

$$F = 9/5C + 32 \text{ or } F = 1.8C + 32$$

To convert from Fahrenheit (F) to Celsius (C):

$$C = (F{-}32)*(5/9) \text{ or } C = (F{-}32)/1.8$$

For example, if the current outside temperature is 80°F and we want the temperature in C, then C = (80-32)/1.8 so C = 26.7°C. If the outside temperature is 30°C and we want to know the temperature in Fahrenheit (F), then F = (30*1.8) + 32 therefore F = 86°.

If you remember some basic information converting from Celsius to Fahrenheit is easy. For every 5 degree increase in temperature in Celsius, the temperature in Fahrenheit increases 9 degrees. For every 1 degree increase in temperature in Celsius, the temperature in Fahrenheit increases 1.8 degrees. The freezing point of water is 0°C or 32°F. So for every 5 degree Celsius increase in temperature add 9 degrees to the Fahrenheit temperature (Table 1.2). So if the temperature in Celsius is 22°, find the temperature in Fahrenheit for 20°C then add 3.6 (2*1.8) to determine the temperature in Fahrenheit (68 + 3.6 = 71.6°F).

Conversions

In science, the metric system is used almost exclusively because of the ease of converting from one scale to another and so others around the world understand what we publish. Therefore, it is important to know how to convert from the metric to the English system and back. Table 1.3 will provide some basic conversion factors to use.

Table 1.2   This shows how easy it is to convert temperature if you just remember a few basic things.

C	°F
0	32
5	41
10	50
15	59
20	68
25	77
30	86
35	95
40	104
45	113
50	122

Table 1.3   Common conversion factors between the English and metric system.

If you know . . .	Multiply by . . .	To get . . .
Inches (in)	2.54	Centimeters (cm)
Feet (ft)	0.305	Meters (m)
Yards (yd)	0.9144	Meters (m)
Miles (mi)	1.61	Kilometers (km)
Gallons (gal)	3.785	Liters (l)
Fluid Ounces (fl oz)	29.57	Milliliters (ml)
Ounces (oz)	28.35	Grams (g)
Pounds (lb)	0.454	Kilograms (kg)
Centimeters (cm)	0.3937	Inches (in)
Meters (m)	3.28	Feet (ft)
Meters (m)	1.09	Yards (yd)
Kilometers (km)	0.621	Miles (mi)
Milliliters (ml)	0.034	Fluid ounces (fl oz)
Liters (l)	0.264	Gallons (gal)
Grams (g)	0.035	Ounces (oz)
Kilograms (kg)	2.2	Pounds (lb)
Kilometers/Hour (KPH)	0.62137	Miles/Hour (MPH)
Acres	4046.856	Square Meters
Acres	0.004046856	Square Kilometers
Quarts	0.25	Gallons
Gallons	4	Quarts
Feet	12	Inches
Pounds	16	Ounces

Rounding Numbers

If you are asked to round numbers always look at the decimal position one place beyond the decimal position you are rounding to. For example, if you are rounding to two decimal places, you must look at the number in the third decimal position to the right of the decimal point to determine how to round the number. If the number in the decimal position you are looking at is 5 or above, increase the number in the prior decimal position by 1 then disregard the remaining decimals. If the number in the decimal position you are looking at is 4 or below, just discard the decimals beyond the position you are rounding to. Table 1.4 gives examples of rounding numbers to 2 decimal places.

Table 1.4   Examples of rounding numbers.

This number . . .	rounds to
1.004	1
1.005	1.01
1.0038	1
1.0051	1.01
9.954	9.95
9.955	9.96
9.991	9.99
9.996	10
9.9549	9.95
9.9551	9.96

The Scientific Method

Anyone who has ever read a mystery novel or seen a "whodunit" on television, has seen the scientific method in action. Anyone who has ever tried to figure out what happens to the refrigerator light when you close the door, or where that other sock goes after you put it in the drier, has used the scientific method. The scientific method is not a mystical, incomprehensible rite that only "polyester plaid" science nerds use to solve esoteric problems. Instead, it is a logical, organized mechanism for identifying and researching a problem, and devising a strategy for solving it.

The scientific method is split up into six major steps:

1. **Determining the problem or question – Observed phenomenon**

   In this step, you (the researcher) must decide what it is that you will be studying. This sounds like a simple procedure, but it is actually very important. It identifies exactly what you wish to learn and it allows you to focus only on that material.

2. **Development of a hypothesis**

   The hypothesis is not just a random W.A.G. (Wild @$$#& Guess) to your problem. Instead, the hypothesis is an educated guess. In other words, it involves researching the problem and finding out what other people have learned, and using that information to help devise an answer. An important aspect of the hypothesis is that it should answer the original question, and it should be testable.

3. **Design an experiment to test the hypothesis**

   Design an experiment whose results will either support or disprove your hypothesis. If your hypothesis is supported, then the results of your experiment will indicate that your hypothesis is correct. However, this does not mean that your hypothesis is 100%, beyond a shadow of a doubt, correct. There may be other factors that will influence the results that you have not tested. Therefore, it is important to say that the hypothesis is supported. You should never say that it is proven. However, the results of your experiment can also prove your hypothesis is wrong!

   There should be at least two groups in your experiment. The first group is the **experimental group**. This group is the group that has the factor that is being tested which is called the **experimental variable**. The experimental variable is the one thing you are changing between the two groups you are testing. It is easy to identify the experimental variable, since it is usually stated in the hypothesis. The second group is the **control group**. The control group is identical to the experimental group in every way, except the control group lacks the experimental variable. If there were other differences, the results of your experiment would be invalidated.

4. **Conduct the experiment and collect the data**

   Run the experiment that you have so carefully constructed. In this step, you will be measuring the dependent variable. This variable (DO NOT confuse it with the experimental variable) is the thing that is being observed or measured. Any pieces of information that you collect regarding the dependent variable are called DATA.

5. **Draw Conclusions from your data – Repeat or Modify**

   Here, it is stated directly whether the hypothesis was supported or disproven. If your hypothesis is supported, it should be repeated, since one of the basic foundations of the scientific method is that it is repeatable. The more an experiment is repeated, the more valid the results are.

   Often times the data will not support the initial hypothesis and further analysis of the problem should be conducted. The analysis of the data will allow the researcher to determine if the hypothesis and experiment should be modified. This can be achieved by changing the experimental variable and deducing a new educated guess on a solution to the initial problem.

   Remember in order for a hypothesis to be supported it must be repeatable.

6. **Final Conclusion – Theory**

   If there is a hypothesis that is supported by many experiments and a lot of data, we call that hypothesis a theory.

   The word theory is often misused in everyday language. Theory and hypothesis are not synonyms. A hypothesis is just an educated guess that perhaps has been supported once or twice by an experiment. A theory was once a hypothesis, but is now supported by a lot of data and is accepted as being correct, until new information is discovered to disprove it. A theory can be disproven at any time through new technology and new discoveries.

If your theory is proven to be verifiable everytime, in every situation without fail, it can be elevated to a **natural law**. Natural laws include Newton's Laws of Motion and gravity.

An Example of the Scientific Method

You are the owner of a nursery and grow roses. You want your rose bushes to produce more blooms so you can increase your sales. You think that adding sugar to the water will cause your rose brushes to produce more blooms and you design an experiment to test your hypothesis. You plant eight rose bushes. Four (A through D) of which you will water without adding sugar which will be your control group. The other four rose bushes you will water with water that you have added sugar to. These four (E through H) will comprise your experimental group. Your experimental variable is the sugar in the water.

You grow the rose bushes for six months carefully counting the number of the blooms that each plant produces. At the end of the growing period, you exam your data which is in the following table.

	Number of Blooms Produced
Rose Bushes A through D	108
Rose Bushes E through H	120

Based on the results, it does seem that adding sugar to the water for your rose bushes increases the number of blooms produced. Should you assume that your hypothesis is correct based on the results of this single experiment? The answer is no. You should repeat the experiment multiple times to confirm your results.

You proceed to run the experiment a second time, however, you decide to not only add sugar to the water but also use a plant light on the experimental group. This would invalidate any results of the experiment because you would not know if the sugar or the light from the plant light caused an increase or decrease in the number of blooms produced. You could create a second experimental group by planting an additional four rose bushes (I through L) and not using the sugar water with that group but using the plant light on your second experimental group. If you want to test multiple experimental variables (sugar and the plant light) you can use multiple experimental groups but you cannot change more than one variable for any one experimental group in a single experiment because you will not know which variable caused a change in the experimental group.

Lab 2

Minerals and Igneous Rocks

Humans have sought out mineral resources since the beginning of society. Without the mineral resources that Earth provides, our lives would be very different than what we currently know. There are currently over 4,000 known minerals; however, only about 30 are common in the crust. During this lab, we will investigate what minerals are and how they are identified. We will then look at how igneous rocks form and are classified.

Atoms, Elements, Isotopes, and Compounds

Before we discuss minerals, we need a basic understanding of the building blocks that make up minerals. An **element** is a fundamental component of matter which cannot be chemically broken down into simpler particles. The elements are arranged in a periodic table (fig. 2.1) based on their atomic number. An **atom** is the basic unit of an element and is about 10^{-10} meters in diameter and is made of three different, smaller particles. A **proton** is a positively charged particle that resides in the **nucleus** (center) of the atom (fig. 2.2). A **neutron** is a particle with no charge that is also located in the nucleus. The neutron has the same mass as the proton. **Electrons** are negatively charged particles that orbit the nucleus of the atom (fig. 2.2). Compared to the proton and neutron, the electron has such little mass that it does not add to the weight of the atom. Every element has an **atomic number** which is a count of the number of protons in the nucleus.

The **atomic mass number** is the sum of the number of protons and neutrons. The number of protons of an element does not change; however, the number of neutrons can vary. An element with a different number of neutrons is called an **isotope**. For example, oxygen (O) has 16 protons in the nucleus and usually has 16 neutrons as well and is ^{16}O. Oxygen can pick up one or two extra neutrons producing ^{17}O or ^{18}O. This changes the atomic mass but not the atomic number and has no impact on the way the oxygen bonds with other elements. Isotopes can be unstable (Uranium-238 or ^{238}U) and will decay to a stable isotope over time. Unstable isotopes are used for dating of rocks and artifacts and well as for energy production. Stable isotopes do not decay over time and are often used as environmental tracers.

If an atom gains or loses an electron, this will affect the charge of the atom making the atom an **ion**. If an extra electron is gained, the atom takes on a negative overall charge and is called an **anion**. If an electron is lost, the atom takes on a positive charge and is called a **cation**. This charge difference can cause atoms to bond together.

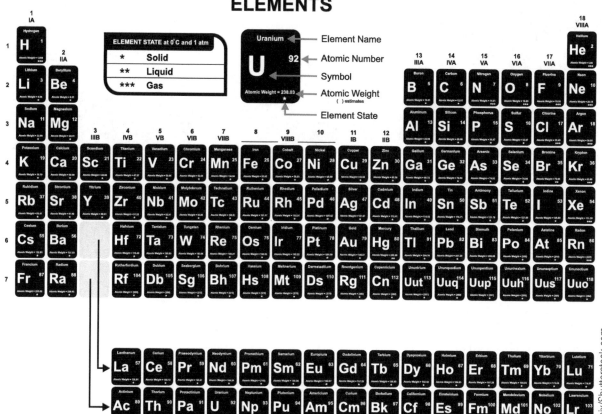

Figure 2.1 The periodic table of the elements arranged by atomic weight.

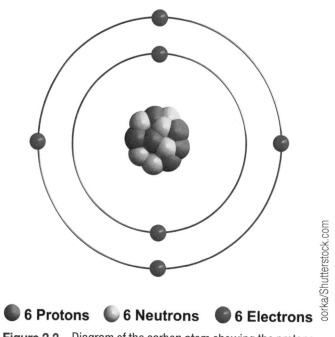

● **6 Protons** ◐ **6 Neutrons** ● **6 Electrons**

Figure 2.2 Diagram of the carbon atom showing the protons and neutrons in the nucleus with the electrons in orbit.

When two atoms chemically bond together because of a difference in their charge an **ionic bond** is formed. The anion will give up an electron to the cation to balance the charge between the two ions. In some cases, anions and cations will share an electron in the outermost orbit of each atom. This is a **covalent bond** between the atoms. When atoms of different elements bond in these manners, they form **compound** which is a chemical combination of two or more elements, in certain proportions, that has a distinct set of physical properties. **Metallic bonds** occur in metals (iron, copper, etc.) and result because the outer electrons in the atoms can freely move from one atom to the next. This increases the density of the material and allows metals to be very good conductors of electricity.

What is a mineral?

A mineral:

1. Must be naturally occurring

2. Be inorganic

3. A definite chemical composition or range of compositions

4. Have a definite internal structure or be a crystalline solid

5. Have distinct physical properties

Some minerals (opal and limonite) do not grow in crystals and lack a definite internal structure. These are sometimes referred to as **mineraloids** as a result. I **strongly** recommend that you learn the definition of a mineral! Let's examine this definition in more detail.

A mineral must be naturally occurring. Ice cubes in your freezer are not minerals, but ice covering a frozen pond is a mineral. Diamonds have been manufactured for industrial purposes since the 1950s. Those diamonds are not minerals because they are man-made. Diamonds used in jewelry are minerals because they formed by natural processes. Man-made diamonds have not reached gemstone quality at this time.

Minerals must be inorganic. While some minerals do contain carbon (C), that carbon is not bonded with the proper elements to be classified as organic carbon like that found in living tissues. Minerals are not produced by living organisms or biologic processes. However, many animals that live in the ocean construct shells using minerals they remove from seawater.

Minerals have a definite chemical composition or range of compositions. All minerals have a chemical formula. For some minerals, this is a fixed formula that does not vary. Quartz (SiO_2), pyrite (FeS_2), and halite ($NaCl$) are examples of this. However, some minerals have a chemical composition that can vary from one end member to another. An example of this is plagioclase feldspar. One end member has a chemical formula which contains 100% calcium (Ca) while the opposite end member contains 100% sodium (Na). So the chemical formula for plagioclase feldspar varies from $CaAl_2Si_2O_8$ to $NaAl_2Si_3O_8$. The percentage of Ca to Na in the formula changes from 0 to 100%, so you could have a plagioclase feldspar with 80% Ca and 20% Na, a 50–50% mix or any other combination.

Have a definite internal structure or be a crystalline solid. At the atomic level, elements bound together in certain specific ways. This results in minerals growing in certain specific shapes (fig. 2.3). For example, halite (NaCl) and pyrite (FeS_2) grow in a cubic form while calcite ($CaCO_3$) grows in a rhombehedral form and fluorite (CaF_3) is octahedral (fig. 2.4). The pyrite samples in your rock kit may not show their crystal structure due to the way pyrite breaks but the calcite and fluorite samples should show some of their crystal structure. The crystal structure is a reflection of the internal atomic order of the mineral. This atomic order is created because of the specific ways that elements bond at the molecular level. This portion of the definition also eliminates liquids and gases from being minerals. For example, naturally occurring ice is a mineral, but water or water vapor is not a mineral because of the lack of an internal bonding order between hydrogen and oxygen in the liquid and gas phases. Mercury is a liquid under normal surface temperature and pressure conditions; however, it does have a distinct bonding order so mercury is considered to be a mineral.

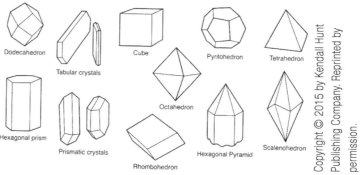

Figure 2.3   Some common crystal forms for minerals. These range from the simple (cubes) to very complex (prismatic crystals and scalenohedrons). From Insights: A Laboratory Manual for Physical & Historical Geology, 5/e by Clair Russell Ossian.

Copyright © 2015 by Kendall Hunt Publishing Company. Reprinted by permission.

Figure 2.4   Pyrite (left) showing cubic crystal structure, calcite (right) showing a rhombehedral crystal structure. The scale bar is in centimeters.

Images courtesy Rick Lynn

Minerals must have distinct physical properties.   Each mineral will exhibit a specific set of characteristics that make it unique. While two minerals may share one or more characteristics, no two minerals will share all of the same characteristics. While two minerals may share the same chemical composition, the crystal structure can be vastly different. In this case, the minerals are called **polymorphs** (fig. 2.5). For example, diamond and graphite are both composed of pure carbon. In diamonds, the carbon atoms are strongly bonded making the diamond very hard. Graphite, on the other hand, has carbon atoms strongly bonded into sheets, but the sheets are bonded together weakly. This allows the sheets to break apart easily. Diamonds are colorless (mostly), clear, and are very hard. Graphite is opaque, dark gray to black, and very soft. Minerals have many other physical properties which we will explore in more detail.

The Arkenstone, iRocks.com

Courtesy of The Arkenstone, iRocks.com

Figure 2.5 The only difference between diamond (left) and graphite (right) is the crystal system they belong to. Graphite is hexagonal but diamond is octahedral.

Cleavage and Fracture. Because of weakness between bonds of certain elements in minerals, the minerals will break in certain specific ways which will reflect their internal atomic structure. This is a property called **cleavage** which is how a mineral breaks. Not all minerals will break on flat surface but instead **fracture** which occurs when minerals break on uneven, irregular surfaces. Micas will break into thin, flat sheets like paper. Other minerals cleave along flat planes at various angles like calcite (rhombehedral, 3 cleavages not at 90°) and plagioclase feldspar (2 cleavages at 90°, fracture in the third direction). Gypsum does have cubic cleavage (3 cleavages at 90°) and cleaves very well in one direction but very poorly in the other two. Figure 2.6 shows the ways that minerals can cleave.

All minerals will grow in a certain crystal form however that does not mean that it will cleave the same way. Quartz will grow in beautiful hexagonal prismatic crystals but does not cleave, instead quartz fractures (fig. 2.7). Pyrite grows in a cube (fig. 2.4) but fractures when it breaks like the sample in your rock kit.

0 No cleavage, only fracture	Irregular masses with no flat surfaces	
1	"Books" that split apart along flat sheets	
2 at 90°	Elongated form with rectangular cross sections (prisms) and parts of such forms	
2 not at 90°	Elongated form with parallelogram cross sections (prisms) and parts of such forms	
3 at 90°	Shapes made of cubes and parts of cubes	
3 not at 90°	Shapes made of rhombohedrons and parts of rhombohedrons	
4	Shapes made of octahedrons and parts of octahedrons	
6	Shapes made of dodecahedrons and parts of dodecahedrons	

Figure 2.6   The various ways in which minerals can cleave.

Figure 2.7   Quartz does not exhibit cleavage instead it fractures on irregular, uneven surfaces (left). Quartz does grow into hexagonal prismatic crystals (right). The scale bar is in centimeters.

Hardness. A German scientist named Frederic Moh created **Moh's Scale of Hardness** (Table 2.1). This is a relative scale of how hard certain minerals are. Moving up the scale from 1 to 10, each mineral is harder or more resistant to scratching than the mineral below it. There are common items used to test hardness as no geologist will carry a sample of each of the minerals on Moh's Scale into the field.

Table 2.1 Moh's Scale of Hardness Courtesy Rick Lynn.

Relative Hardness	Common Items for Comparison
1-Talc	
2-Gypsum	
	2.5-Fingernail
3-Calcite	3.0–3.5 Copper Penny
4-Flourite	
	4.5-Carpenter's Nail
5-Apatite	
	5.5-Glass
6-Orthoclase Feldspar	
	6.5-Streak Plate
7-Quartz	
8-Topaz	
9-Corundum	
10-Diamond	

Try to scratch the talc or gypsum samples in your rock kit with your fingernail. You should be able to scratch them easily. Now try to scratch the calcite, plagioclase feldspar, or quartz sample with your fingernail. These minerals are harder than your fingernail so nothing happens. However, the quartz sample will scratch the plagioclase feldspar or calcite samples.

Luster. Luster is how a mineral reflects light. Some minerals have a metallic luster and reflect light like metal such as pyrite and galena. There are numerous terms to describe non-metallic luster. Quartz is said to have a vitreous (glassy) luster because it reflects light like glass. A few other descriptors for non-metallic luster include earthy (like soil), greasy, pearly (like a pearl), and silky.

Streak. When powdered a mineral will often have a different color. Streak is the true color of a mineral. If you write on a chalkboard with chalk, the chalk is becoming powered and you are observing the color of the streak of the chalk. The mineral hematite (Fe_2O_3) can be found in a variety of colors (fig. 2.8), but its streak color is always reddish-brown. Use the streak plate in your rock kit to observe the streak color of the hematite in your rock kit.

Specific Gravity. Specific gravity is the weight of a substance compared to the weight of an equal volume of water. The specific gravity of minerals can vary greatly and can be easily tested just by bouncing two minerals in each hand. While this will not give you the exact value for specific gravity for that mineral, it is often enough to help with the identification of the mineral. Place the

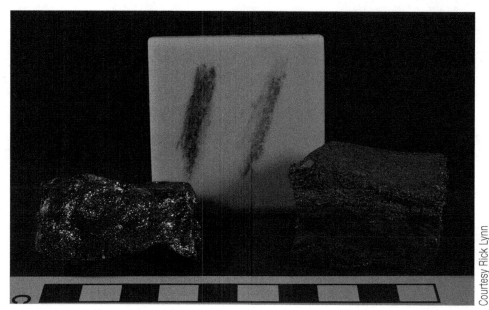

Courtesy Rick Lynn

Figure 2.8   Two samples of the mineral hematite. The color of the samples is nothing alike but the streak color for both is reddish-brown.

Table 2.2   Specific gravity of some common minerals compared to water. Courtesy Rick Lynn.

Substance	Specific Gravity
Water	1.0
Sulfur	2.1
Graphite	2.0–2.3
Gypsum	2.3
Quartz	2.7
Mica	2.7–3.1
Flourite	3.0–3.3
Pyrite	4.9–5.2
Galena	7.5–7.6
Copper	8.8–9.0
Gold	19.0

galena and quartz samples in your hands and bounce them up and down. You will easily notice that the galena "feels" heavier due to the higher specific gravity of galena (7.5-7.6) compared to quartz (2.7). A list of some common minerals and their specific gravity can be found in table 2.2.

Color. People are visually oriented and react to color immediately. While color can be a useful tool when doing mineral identification, it can also cause great confusion and should be used with extreme caution. Some minerals will almost always have the same color. For example, the mineral olivine (($Fe,Mg)_2SiO_4$) is so named because of the unique olive green color. The mineral malachite ($Cu_2CO_3(OH)_2$) is a dark green color while azurite ($Cu_3(CO_3)_2(OH)_2$) is a deep, rich blue (fig. 2.9).

Figure 2.9 Malachite (left) is always a deep green while azurite (right) is dark blue. The scale bar is in centimeters.

Courtesy Rick Lynn

Courtesy of The Arkenstone, iRocks .com

Images courtesy of Rick Lynn

Figure 2.10 Various samples of fluorite. The scale bar is in centimeters.

Care must be taken when using color for mineral identification. Quartz (SiO_2) can be found in almost any color under the Sun. Quartz can be found that is clear, gray, white, pink, reddish-brown, black, purple, and amber. Because of the variation in color, many of these varieties of quartz were given names before it was realized they were all the same thing. Purple quartz is amethyst, amber quartz is called citrine, opaque red or yellow quartz is called jasper, and the list goes on. Fluorite is another common mineral that is found in a multitude of colors (fig. 2.10).

Images courtesy of Rick Lynn

Figure 2.11   Plagioclase feldspar with striations (left) and orthoclase feldspar which lack striations (right). The scale bar is in centimeters.

Specific Properties. Many minerals have properties that are specific to them. For example, the mineral magnetite (Fe_3O_4) is magnetic. Calcite will react (fizz) in hydrochloric acid (HCl). Orthoclase and plagioclase feldspars have the same hardness, crystal habit, and cleavage; however, plagioclase feldspars contain parallel laminations on their surface called **striations** which orthoclase feldspars lack (fig. 2.11). The mineral halite (table salt) can be identified by taste.

Types of minerals

Minerals are placed into broad groups based on the primary elements the minerals are made of. There are two major groups which are broken down into subcategories within those groups.

Silicates. The two most common elements in Earth's crust are oxygen (O) and silicon (Si). Therefore, the largest of the mineral groups are the silicates which all contain significant quantities of oxygen and silicon. This group of minerals is subdivided based on how the silicon and oxygen bound together. The most basic building block of the silicate group is the **silicate tetrahedra** in which one silicon is surrounded by four oxygens and forms a pyramid structure (fig. 2.12). These tetrahedra then bound together to form chains, sheets, or three dimensional frameworks as the oxygens are shared between molecules (fig. 2.12). The most common silicate minerals in the crust are the feldspars and quartz.

Ferromagnesians are common silicate minerals that also contain iron (Fe) and magnesium (Mg). These minerals tend to be less stable at the surface and weather quickly. The **micas** are a group of sheet silicates that are high in potassium (K) and aluminum (Al). Micas tend to weather rapidly to another group of silicates known as **clays**. Clays are also sheet silicates in which the sheets can easily "slide" past each other giving some clays a slippery feel. Some clays are known as "expansive clays" because when they absorb water they expand then shrink when they dry out. This creates huge problems with structures which are built on soils rich in expansive clays.

Nonsilicates. These minerals contain a variety of base elements that comprise their crystal structure but do not contain silicon and oxygen together.

The **carbonates** contain carbon (C) and oxygen (O) in their crystal structure. Specifically, these minerals contain one carbon combined with three oxygens so all will have (CO_3) anion in the

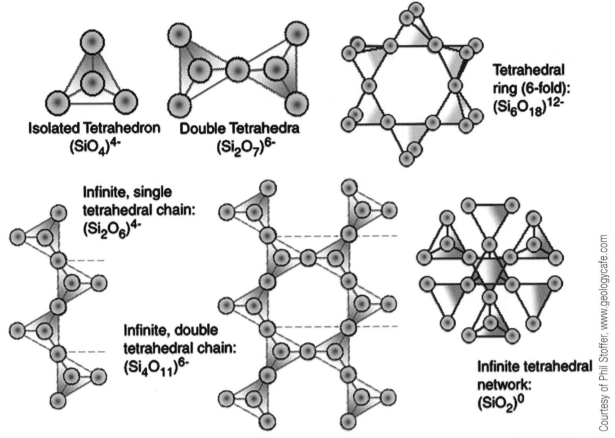

Figure 2.12   The most basic building block of the silicate group is the silicate tetrahedra in which one silicon is bounded with four oxygens in a pyramid-like structure. These tetrahedra then bond to form more complex crystal structures in other silicate minerals.

chemical formula. These minerals dissolve easily in water especially if it is slightly acidic. The most common of the carbonate minerals is calcite ($CaCO_3$). The world's oceans contain large quantities of dissolved calcite which can recrystallize and form a rock we know as limestone. The next most common carbonate mineral is dolomite ($Ca,Mg(CO_3)$). Dolomite has had part of the calcium (Ca) replaced with magnesium (Mg) in the crystal structure. Pure dolomite is a 50–50% mix of Ca and Mg but, as with the plagioclase feldspars, the percentage can vary producing minerals with different names based on the exact percentage. Pure magnesium carbonate ($Mg(CO_3)$) is called magnesite. Many other elements can substitute for the Ca in the crystal structure forming a variety of carbonate minerals such as rhodochrosite ($Mn(CO_3)$), siderite ($Fe(CO_3)$), and ankerite ($Ca,Mg,Fe(CO_3)$). The **sulfate** minerals all contain sulfur (S) and oxygen in a 1:4 ratio (SO_4). The most common sulfate mineral is gypsum ($CaSO_4 \cdot 2H_2O$).

Sulfide minerals contain sulfur but without the oxygen. A common sulfide mineral is pyrite (FeS_2). While not used as a source of iron, pyrite can be problematic when exposed at the surface because it readily breaks down in the presence of water and produces sulfuric acid as a by-product. Pyrite is commonly found in waste piles at mine sites. Another common sulfide mineral is galena (PbS) which is a valued source of lead and is named after a town in Illinois. Copper (Cu), zinc (Z), magnesium (Mg), and manganese (Mn) are also commonly found bonded with sulfur.

Oxides contain one or more metals combined with oxygen. These include minerals such as magnetite (Fe_3O_4) and hematite (Fe_2O_3).

Native elements are elements composed of only one chemical. These commonly include metals such as gold (Au) and silver (Ag) as well as other elements like sulfur and graphite.

What is a Rock?

A **rock** is a solid, cohesive aggregate of one or more minerals or mineral materials. Rocks contain a record of their history based on the minerals grains in the rock and how those grains fit together. There are three categories of rocks: igneous, sedimentary, and metamorphic. The categories are differentiated by the method in which the rock forms.

Types of Rocks

Igneous – Formed from cooled magma or lava.

Sedimentary – Formed when sediment becomes cemented or compacted (lithified).

Metamorphic – Pre-existing rock altered by heat, pressure, hot fluids, or a combination of these.

The rock cycle is a very important concept for this course (fig. 2.13). This process does not work as a big, continuous loop; the cycle can be crossed at any point. For example, igneous rocks can be metamorphosed if heat & pressure are applied. Metamorphic rocks may be eroded to form sediments which become sedimentary rocks. Sedimentary rocks may be melted and become magma forming igneous rocks.

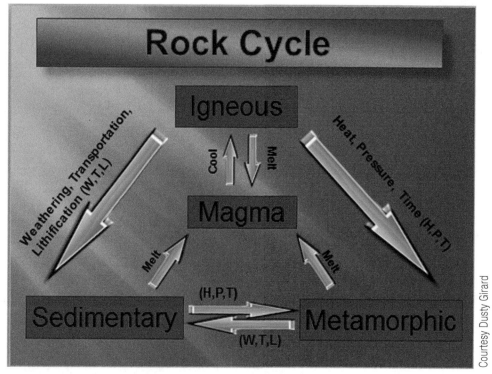

Figure 2.13   The Rock Cycle.

Igneous Rocks

Igneous rocks form as molten material solidifies during cooling. The molten material is called **magma** which is naturally occurring molten rock. When magma flows onto the Earth's surface, it is called **lava**. Depending on the minerals in the magma, temperatures must range from 300 to 1,100°C in order for the magma to remain molten. As the magma cools, different minerals form under different temperature and pressure conditions which impacts the way igneous rocks are named. **Bowen's reaction series** (fig. 2.14) is based on experimental data collected by Normal L. Bowen in the early 1900s while working at Carnegie Institution of Washington. This experimental model helps us to understand the temperature conditions under which minerals form thus providing insight into why certain igneous rocks contain specific mineral combinations. Remember, this information is based on a laboratory experiment under controlled conditions. In the real world, this sequence does not always produce the same results as the laboratory model.

On the discontinuous branch, as temperature decreases, minerals will form in the temperature zone where they are most stable. Once the temperature drops below the perfect temperature range for that mineral, the bonds holding the elements together will break and the elements that formed the mineral return to the magma mixture to be used to make other minerals.

On the continuous branch, the percentage of calcium (Ca) vs sodium (Na) slowly changes as the Ca in the magma is used up. This branch produces the plagioclase feldspars. The two branches converge and minerals high in potassium (K), aluminum (Al), and silica (Si) begin to form.

Rocks created from these minerals will melt in the reverse order of the mineral formation (bottom to top).

Naming igneous rocks-mineral assemblages

Igneous rocks are named based on their mineral composition and their texture. On the right side of Figure 2.14, you will notice three terms: mafic, intermediate, and felsic. These terms are defined based on the silica (SiO_2) content of the igneous rock, and the terms are derived from the primary mineral constituents of the rocks.

Rocks with a very low silica content ($<45\%$) are called **ultramafic** and are rich in iron (Fe) and magnesium (Mg). These rocks form at very high temperature in the upper part of the mantle. Because of the conditions under which they form, they are rarely found on the surface. If these rocks do find their way to the surface, they weather rapidly because they are very unstable under the temperature and pressure conditions found on the Earth's surface. The most common ultramafic rock is peridotite (fig. 2.15).

Mafic rocks have a SiO_2 content between 45 and 52% and are rich in iron (Fe), magnesium (Mg) and calcium (Ca). The name is derived from the primary elements that make up these rocks, magnesium, and iron. These rocks are not extremely stable under surface conditions and weather rapidly. Basalt and gabbro are common examples of mafic rocks (fig. 2.16).

Rocks that are classified as **intermediate** have a silica content between 52 and 65%. These rocks have lower quantities of Fe, Mg, and Ca and are becoming richer in sodium (Na), potassium (K), and aluminum (Al). These rocks are moderately stable under surface conditions and weather more slowly than mafic rocks. Andesite and diorite are common examples of intermediate rocks (fig. 2.17).

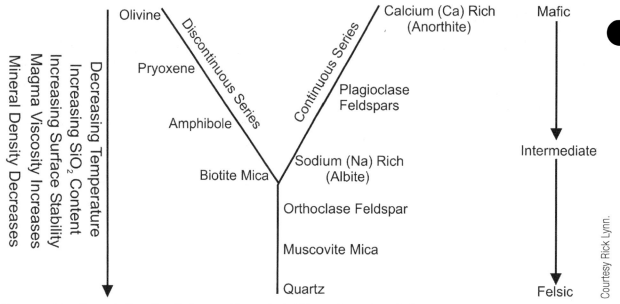

Figure 2.14　Bowen's Reaction Series provides an insight into when minerals form as magma cools. This laboratory experiment is a "perfect case" scenario and is often different in the real world.

Figure 2.15　Samples of the rock peridotite which forms under high pressure and temperature conditions which occur near the crust-mantle boundary. The scale bar is in centimeters.

Felsic rocks have a silica greater than 65%. These rocks are rich in potassium (K) and aluminum (Al). The name is derived from the feldspars and silica which are the primary component of these rocks. These rocks are extremely stable under surface conditions and weather slowly because of the low temperatures under which they form. Rhyolite and granite are common examples of felsic rocks (fig. 2.18).

Naming igneous rocks-textures

The **texture** of igneous rocks refers to the size of the mineral grains that are in the rock. This is a result of the length of time the magma or lava has to cool. Magma remains within the crust of the

Images courtesy Rick Lynn

Figure 2.16   Samples of the rock basalt (left) and gabbro (right). The dark color is an indicator of high concentrations of iron (Fe) and magnesium (Mg). These mafic rocks have a silica content between 45 and 52%. The scale bar is in centimeters.

Images courtesy Rick Lynn

Figure 2.17   Samples of the intermediate igneous rocks andesite (left) and diorite (right). Intermediate igneous rocks are often said to have a "salt and pepper" appearance due to the roughly equal mix of light- and dark-colored minerals. The scale bar is in centimeters.

Images courtesy Rick Lynn

Figure 2.18   The images above are the felsic igneous rocks rhyolite (left) and granite (right). The lighter colors are an indication of minerals with increased silica content, aluminum (Al), and potassium (K). The scale bar is in centimeters.

Earth and is insulted by the rock surrounding the magma body. Therefore, the magma cools slowly over long periods of time (think geologic time here!). Lava is exposed on the Earth's surface where the temperature is far below that of the molten material resulting in rapid cooling.

Igneous rocks that cool over long periods of time allow the mineral crystals to grow for longer periods and become larger. These are called **plutonic** or **intrusive** igneous rocks. Plutonic igneous rocks have a **phaneritic** texture which means the mineral grains are large enough to see with the naked eye. Gabbro, diorite, and granite (Figs. 2.16, 2.17, and 2.18 respectively) all have a phaneritic texture. In some cases, the mineral crystals in plutonic rocks get very large and have a **pegmatitic** texture. For a rock to be classified as a pegmatite, the average size of the mineral crystals must be at least 1cm. There is no upper limit on the size of pegmatites so crystals can grow to several meters in size (fig. 2.19).

If the magma reaches the surface and becomes lava, it will cool rapidly forming **volcanic** or **extrusive** igneous rocks. Volcanic igneous rocks contain mineral crystals which are to small to see with the naked eye because they cooled quickly producing an **aphanitic** texture. Rhyolite, andesite, and basalt all have an aphanitic texture (figs. 2.16, 2.17, and 2.18, respectively). If magma is extruded into an ocean, the resulting rock will contain no mineral crystals at all because of the extremely rapid rate of cooling. These igneous rocks are classified as having a **glassy** texture such as obsidian (fig. 2.20). You may be able to see individual minerals grains in an aphanitic rock with a hand lens, but you will not see mineral grains in a glassy rock under any circumstances because no mineral grains exist.

In some cases, magma that has been cooling slowly is suddenly extruded onto the surface. The resulting rock will contain some mineral crystals large enough to see but they will be contained in a groundmass of material with mineral grains that are too small to see with the naked eye. Basically, this rock is a mixture of phaneritic and aphanitic textures and is said to have a **porphyritic** texture (fig. 2.21).

During a volcanic eruption, pieces of magma can be ejected into the atmosphere and cool rapidly. If that magma contains large amounts of trapped gas, pore space can form within the rock as it cools producing a **frothy** or **vesicular** texture (fig. 2.22). The solid portion of the rock will have a glassy texture however, because of the large amount of gas trapped within the rock the rock will be light enough to float on water.

Courtesy Rick Lynn

Figure 2.19   A sample of a pegmatitic granite from the Tishomingo Formation in southern Oklahoma. The large orange to pink grains are orthoclase feldspar, the white to gray grains are quartz, and the dark gray to black grains are amphibole. The scale bar is in centimeters.

Figure 2.20   The image above is the igneous rock obsidian which is also known as volcanic glass. The glassy texture is an indication of extremely rapid cooling which did not allow any minerals grains to form. The scale bar is in centimeters.

Figure 2.21   This is an example of a porphyritic texture. Note the large crystals contained in a groundmass of aphanitic texture. The scale bar is in centimeters.

Images courtesy Rick Lynn

Figure 2.22   The rocks pumice (left) and scoria (right) formed as magma solidified rapidly around gas bubbles that were trapped in the magma. Pumice is typically white to light gray while scoria is typically dark red to black. The scale bar is in centimeters.

The following table is used to classify igneous rocks. Determine the texture (left column) then the mineral composition and the rock can be easily named. Rocks with a glassy texture contain no mineral grains and are always called obsidian.

Mineral Composition			
Texture	Felsic	Intermediate	Mafic	Ultramafic
Aphanitic	Rhyolite	Andesite	Basalt	
Phaneritic	Granite	Diorite	Gabbro	Peridotite
Porphyritic	Rhyolite Porphyry	Andesite Porphyry	Basalt Porphyry	
Pegmatitic	Granite Pegmatite	Diorite Pegmatite	Gabbro Pegmatite	
Glassy	Obsidian			
Vesicular	Pumice	Scoria		

Sedimentary and Metamorphic Rocks

Sedimentary Rocks

Sediment is loose, unconsolidated accumulations of weathered mineral grains and rock fragments that have been transported by wind, water, or ice then deposited at some location. As the sediment becomes compacted and/or cemented together in a process called **lithification**, the sediment is transformed into **sedimentary rock**. The sedimentary rock forms under temperatures and pressures at or near those found on the surface and will be more compact and dense than the sediment the rock formed from. Some sedimentary rocks form from solution. There are several major groups of sedimentary rocks: clastic, chemical, and biochemical (bioclastic).

Types of Sedimentary Rock

Clastic sedimentary rocks are formed from broken fragments (called **clasts**) of minerals and other rocks. Minerals and rocks on the surface are constantly under attack by a variety of forces including rain, windblown particles, waves, ice, and plants that cause the rocks to be broken into smaller and smaller pieces. These clasts are then transported to different locations and deposited as sediment. In time geologic forces may turn this unconsolidated sediment into clastic sedimentary rocks (i.e. shale, siltstone, sandstone, etc.). Clastic sedimentary rocks are named based on their mineral composition (fig. 3.1), the size of the particles that make up the rock (fig. 3.2), and the roundness of the grains (fig. 3.3). Note that sand refers to a grain size and has nothing to do with mineral composition. A boulder is anything larger than 25.6cm (that is approximately 10 inches for those of you who are metrically challenged!).

When sediment is deposited, the grains will not stack together perfectly. This will leave space between the grains of the sediment called pore space. This pore space allows sediment and sedimentary rock to store fluids such as water or hydrocarbons. This pore space can be partly or completely destroyed when sediment is turned into sedimentary rock.

Lithification, also called **diagenesis**, is the process of turning sediment into sedimentary rock. Since clastic sediments are often transported by water, the water will fill the pore space of the sediment after deposition. Clastic sediments become compacted as the water is driven off during burial by the weight of overlying material as more sediment is deposited on top of existing sediment.

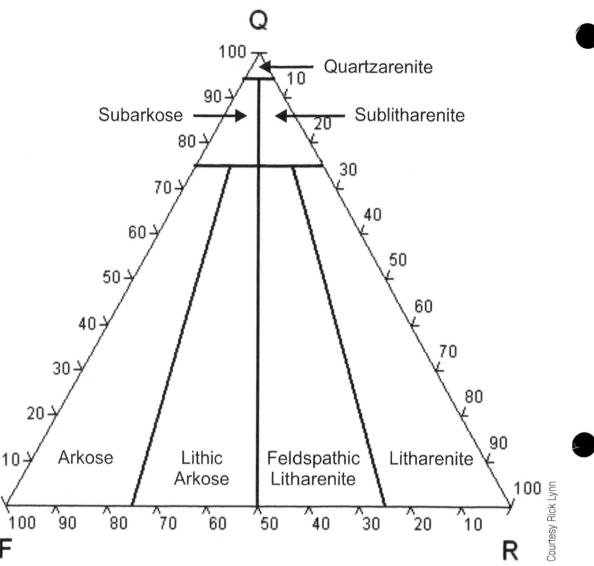

Figure 3.1   This ternary diagram is used to name different types of sandstone based on mineral composition. The name is determined based on the percentage of quartz (Q), feldspar (F), and rock fragments (R) found in the sandstone.

Compaction decreases the amount of pore space and can cause the grains to become distorted and can lock clastic grains together forming sedimentary rocks such as shale or mudstone.

As fluids flow through the pore space in sediment or sedimentary rock minerals can precipitate out in the pore space between the grains thus cementing the rock together. **Cementation** occurs as the grains become locked together due to the growth of these new minerals. The most common cement is calcite followed by quartz and clay minerals. The process of compaction and cementation both reduce pore space between the grains and hold the sediment together turning the sediment into sedimentary rock.

Common clastic sedimentary rocks are mudstone or shale which are composed of clay size particles and are typically dominated by quart grains (fig. 3.4); siltstone (silt size grains) will also mostly contain quartz (fig. 3.5); sandstone (sand size grains) may contain a variety of mineral grains which

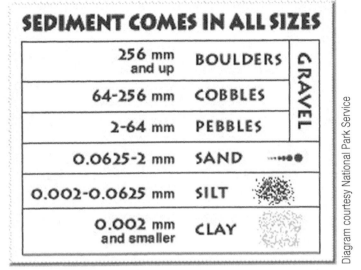

Figure 3.2   The Wentworth Grain Size Scale of sediment size. Clay and silt size particles are too small to distinguish with the naked eye.

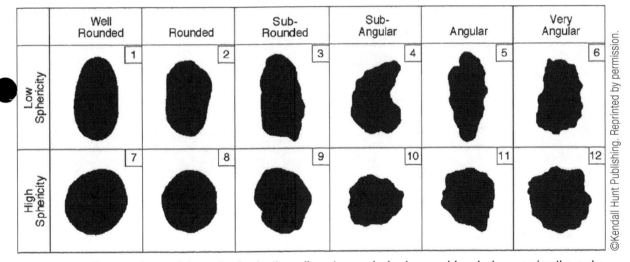

Figure 3.3   The roundness of the grains in clastic sedimentary rocks is also considered when naming the rocks.

determine the specific name for the sandstone (fig. 3.1 and 3.5). Clastic sedimentary rocks made of larger grains are primarily named based on the angularity of the particles. Brecchia (fig. 3.6) and conglomerate (fig. 3.7) contain grains that are gravel size. The grains in brecchia are angular whereas the grains in conglomerate are rounded.

Chemical sedimentary rocks form by the precipitation of minerals from a solution (water). As water flows into a confined basin, the concentration of minerals in the water increases and evaporation will also increase the concentration of minerals in the water. If the water becomes over saturated, the minerals will begin to crystallize out of the solution and fall to the bottom forming layers of sedimentary rock such as limestone, rock salt (halite), and rock gypsum. The Great Salt Flats in Utah are the result of chemical precipitation of minerals as Lake Bonneville evaporated leaving the Great Salt Lake behind as a remnant.

Figure 3.4   Shale is made of clay size sediment. Shale will often break along fairly flat surfaces. The scale bar is in centimeters.

Figure 3.5   The grains in siltstone (left) are too small to easily distinguish with the naked eye. Sandstone (right) is a common sedimentary rock composed of sand-size grains. The grains in sandstone will often consists of quartz, feldspar, and rock fragments. The scale bar is in centimeters.

Figure 3.6   The sedimentary rock called brecchia is made of gravel-size particles that are angular. The scale bar is in centimeters.

Figure 3.7 Note the well-rounded, gravel-size grains in this conglomerate from Oregon. The scale bar is in centimeters.

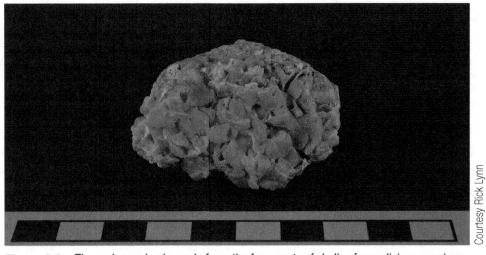

Figure 3.8 The rock coquina is made from the fragments of shells of once living organisms.

Sedimentary rocks form from the remains of once living organisms are called **biochemical** or **bioclastic** rocks. If the rock is composed of clasts of shell fragments of once living organisms, they are bioclastic sedimentary rocks. The most common bioclastic sedimentary rocks are limestone and coquina (fig. 3.8). Because most living organisms that make shells create them from calcite $(CaCO_3)$, limestone will react with HCl just as the mineral calcite does.

Figure 3.9 Coal forms as plant material accumulates and becomes lithified into rock. The scale bar is in centimeters.

Coal (fig. 3.9) is another bioclastic sedimentary rock that forms from the remains of plants. As plant debris accumulate in swampy, low oxygen environments, the plant material becomes compacted until it turns into coal. There are various grades of coal including (from low to high) lignite, sub-bituminous, bituminous, and a metamorphosed version called anthracite. With increasing grade, the amount of energy released when the coal burns increases due to the carbon content of the coal increasing. Higher grade coal also produces less pollution than lower grades because higher grade coal includes less nitrogen and sulfur.

What can we learn about the environment from sedimentary rocks?

As the grains that become clastic sedimentary rocks are transported, they become more rounded and more spherical (fig. 3.3). The distance the grains have been transported from the source area (called the provenance) can be inferred from the level of rounding and sphericity. Grains that have been moved short distances will be angular, but grains that have been transported long distances and moved multiple times will be very rounded and become more spherical.

Grain size (fig. 3.2) can provide information about the level of energy in the depositional system. A **depositional system** is the location where transported sediment is deposited. It simply takes more energy to move large grains than it does small ones. Clay and silt-sized particles are easy to move and are only deposited on low energy environments. If sand size or larger particles were deposited, the energy in the system had to be much higher.

When sediment is deposited, it can form horizontal layers that are parallel to the surface (at the time of deposition) which is called **bedding** (fig. 3.10). If sediment is deposited by moving water or wind, one layer can become truncated before another layer of sediment is deposited on top of it which is called **cross-bedding** (fig. 3.11). Why do we care? because the size of the cross-beds tells us about the depositional environment. If very large-scale cross-beds are formed, it indicates that the material was deposited by wind instead of water.

Figure 3.10 Horizontal bedding in sandstone with thin layers of mudstone. The sandstone was deposited during time of higher flow levels (flooding) and the mudstone was deposited in calm water.

Figure 3.11 Cross bedding in sandstone. Large cross beds (left) only form when sand is deposited by wind. Small scale cross bedding (centimeters) in the result of sand being deposited by flowing water (right).

Ripple marks form as sediment is deposited by moving fluids. If the ripple marks are asymmetric (fig. 3.12) that indicates the fluid was flowing in a single direction. If the fluid was flowing back and forth during the deposition of the sediment, the ripple marks that are created will be symmetric (fig. 3.13).

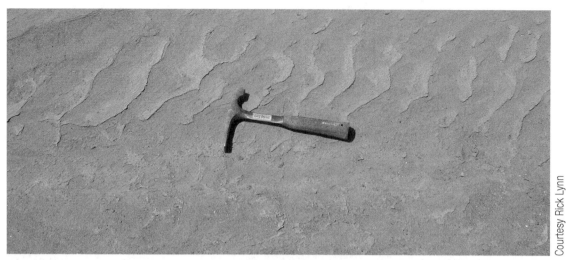

Figure 3.12   Asymmetric ripple marks in freshly deposited fine-grained sand. The flow direction would be toward the handle of the rock hammer. The rock hammer is approximately 30 cm in length.

Figure 3.13   Symmetric ripple marks created in fine-grained sand before lithification.

Mud or **dissection cracks** are formed when clay-size sediment dries out. As the sediment dries, it shrinks causing five or six-sided polygonal structures to form. Clay-size particles are only deposited in very low energy environments such as floodplains or between channels of a delta. After a flood recedes, the sediment thin dries out creating mud cracks (fig. 3.14).

Figure 3.14   The photos above are examples of mud cracks that formed in clay-size sediment of drive river beds and floodplains. The rock hammer is approximately 30 cm in length.

Metamorphic Rocks

As preexisting rocks are subjected to heat, pressure, and/or chemically active fluids, they are altered into **metamorphic** rocks. The term metamorphic comes from the Greek "meta" meaning to change and "morph" means shape. Metamorphic rocks undergo changes that impact the size of mineral grains as well as their chemistry. Some minerals may grow into larger crystals whereas other minerals may be destroyed and replaced by new mineral assemblages in the rock.

There are two types of metamorphic rocks. **Foliated** rocks have bands of minerals aligned parallel to each other in layers (fig. 3.15). Foliated metamorphic rocks are defined based on their **metamorphic grade** which indicates how much the original or parent rock was modified. In low-grade foliated

Figure 3.15   This foliated metamorphic rock is called gneiss. The dark and light bands are caused by the parallel alignment of minerals in the rock. The lighter bands are orthoclase feldspar and the darker bands are biotite mica. The scale bar is in centimeters.

rocks, the banding may not be apparent because the mineral grains have not had time to grow large enough to see which occurs in slate. Even if the foliation results from mineral grains which are too small to see, the rock will still break along the planes of foliation because of weakness in the molecular bonds in the minerals (cleavage). This property allows slate to be broken into sheets and used for chalkboards and shingles. As the metamorphic grade increases, the foliation becomes more clear because the mineral grains have been exposed to higher temperature and pressure conditions for a longer period of time allowing the mineral grains to grow larger. The parent rock for most foliated metamorphic rocks is shale or mudstone.

Metamorphic grade is determined based on the specific minerals that are contained in the rock. Minerals are stable under different temperature and pressure conditions as was discussed in lab 2 when Bowen's Reaction Series was covered. Thus as metamorphic grade increases, different minerals will form based on the specific temperature and pressure conditions the parent rock was subjected to. For example, slate (low grade) is mostly composed of muscovite mica but phyllite (low grade) will also contain the mineral chlorite. Schist (medium grade) can contain biotite and muscovite mica but often contains garnet, staurolite and may contain quartz and feldspar. Gneiss (high grade) typically contains quartz, feldspar and may contain sillimanite. By studying the specific minerals in metamorphic rocks, the metamorphic grade can be determined.

Low-grade metamorphic rocks include slate and phyllite (fig. 3.16). Both slate and phyllite contain minerals grains too small to see with the naked eye. Slate commonly contains muscovite mica grains that have aligned themselves parallel to each other as the parent rock was altered. Because muscovite cleaves into thin sheets, slate will also cleave producing very flat surfaces on the rock. The muscovite mica can be seen in slate when viewed in thin section under a microscope (fig. 3.17). Phyllite will also contain the mineral chlorite and the minerals grains in phyllite will be large enough to reflect light which will give the rock a brushed metallic sheen as light easily reflects off the muscovite mica grains.

Images courtesy Rick Lynn

Figure 3.16   Samples of slate (left) and phyllite. Slate can be found in a variety of colors and does not show foliation well because of the small size of the mineral grains. The lines on the side of the slate samples are where the rock would break along the alignment of muscovite mica. Phyllite (right) will reflect light well giving the rock a shiny, semi-metallic look. The scale bar is in centimeters.

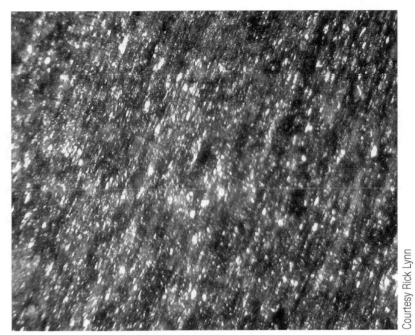

Figure 3.17 In this photomicrograph, the parallel alignment of the muscovite mica grains in slate can be clearly seen.

Figure 3.18 A biotite-muscovite schist. The mineral grains have become large enough to clearly see producing a "scaly" appearance. The scale bar is in centimeters.

Increased metamorphism produces a foliated metamorphic rock called schist (fig. 3.18). The mineral grains in schist can be clearly seen and the parallel alignment of the mineral grains will be clear. Muscovite and biotite mica are common in schist as well as the minerals garnet and staurolite. Large mica minerals will often give schist a "scaly" appearance. In some cases, garnet and staurolite grains will become very large in schist, and these large grains are called porphyroblasts (fig. 3.19).

Figure 3.19   A muscovite mica, garnet, staurolite schist with porphyroblast of garnet (angular), and staurolite (elongated) minerals. The scale bar is in centimeters.

High-grade metamorphism will produce a foliated metamorphic rock named gneiss (pronounced like nice, fig. 3.15). The parallel alignment of the mineral grains in gneiss will be very clear. Gneiss will often contain biotite mica, quartz, and orthoclase (potassium) feldspar. Because of the mineral assemblage of gneiss, granite is often the parent rock as granite will commonly contain the same minerals.

Nonfoliated metamorphic rocks are comprised of interlocking crystals and do not have the banded appearance that foliated metamorphic rocks do. These rocks form as the temperature and pressure allow the mineral grains of the parent rock to grow larger. Unlike foliated metamorphic rocks, the chemistry of nonfoliated metamorphic rocks is not changed.

A common nonfoliated metamorphic rock is marble (fig. 3.20) which is the end product of metamorphosing limestone. Remember that limestone is made of the mineral calcite but is very fine grained so that the individual mineral crystals cannot be seen. After metamorphism, marble is still made of calcite but the mineral crystals have just had time to grow so they are easy to see. Because marble and limestone are both made of the mineral calcite, they will react with a weak solution of hydrochloric acid (HCl). Quartzite (fig. 3.21) is a metamorphosed version of quartz-rich sandstone. The quartz grains of the parent rock have been cemented together with quartz cement due to heat and pressure. Quartzite is a very strong, durable rock. The quartz grains are so well cemented that quartzite will break through the mineral grains instead of breaking around them.

Types of Metamorphism

There are four ways that can be metamorphosed. **Contact metamorphism** occurs when magma comes in contact with preexisting (country) rock. The area around the magma is literally "baked" by the heat creating an area of metamorphic rock near the contact called a **metamorphic halo**

Figure 3.20   Marble is a metamorphosed version of limestone. The calcite mineral grains in the rock have become large enough to clearly see.

Figure 3.21   This is a sample of the metamorphic rock quartzite. Quartzite forms when a quartz-rich sandstone is cemented with quartz cement. This produces a very strong, durable rock. The scale bar is in centimeters.

(fig. 3.22). Larger intrusions will cause more metamorphism due to the larger contact area around the intrusion. Mafic magma will be hotter than felsic magma thus a mafic intrusion will create a larger area of metamorphism as the heat will penetrate the country rock further away from the intrusion.

Burial metamorphism is caused as material becomes buried deeper in the Earth. The weight of the overlying material causes an increase in temperature. This increase in temperature with depth is called the **geothermal gradient** which, on average, is about 30°C/km (fig. 3.23).

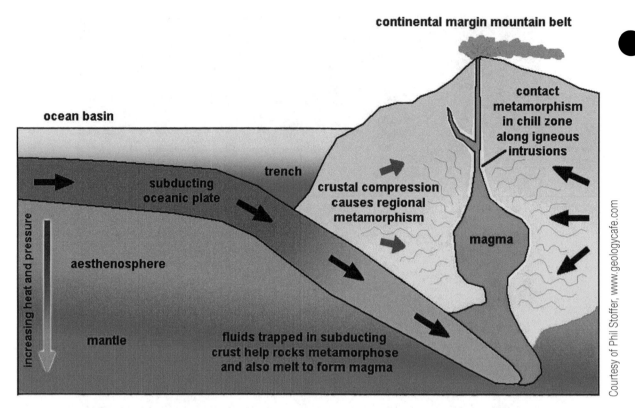

Figure 3.22   The heat from a magma body will cause the rocks around it to be metamorphosed producing a metamorphic halo as shown in yellow around the magma.

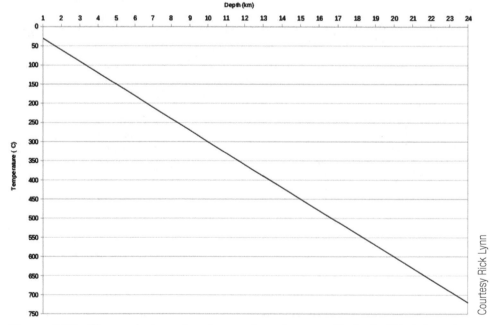

Figure 3.23   The graph shows how temperature changes with depth. This is based on an average surface temperature of 25°C.

Regional metamorphism (fig. 3.22) covers 100s of square km and is typically associated with mountain building and tectonic events. At convergent plate boundaries, the collision will create pressure and heat with higher levels of metamorphism located near the interior of the collision zone with decrease in metamorphism when moving away from the interior. Convergent plate boundaries will also create melting of the subducting plate which generates additional heat for metamorphic processes. Therefore, the metamorphic grade will vary moving across the area depending on the heat and pressure applied in a specific location.

Hot fluids flowing through rocks will alter them physically and chemically in a process known as **hydrothermal** metamorphism. Magma will always contain a certain amount of water which will follow fractures in country rock leading away from the magma chamber. The hot, mineral rich water will alter the country rocks as it flows away from the magma chamber. Groundwater will also be heated by the magma intrusion leading the hydrothermal alteration of the country rock.

Water Usage

Water on Earth; Where it came from and where it goes

Water is practically everywhere on Earth. Moreover, it is the only known substance that can naturally exist as a gas, a liquid, and solid within the relatively small range of air temperatures and pressures found at the Earth's surface. The hydrologic cycle explains the constant circulation of water between the atmosphere, biosphere, land, and sea, but it does not give a clear picture of how much water the Earth actually contains. In all, the Earth's water content is about 1.39 billion cubic kilometers (331 million cubic miles), with the bulk of it, about 97.5%, being in the global oceans. As for the rest, approximately 1.8% is stored in the polar icecaps, glaciers, and permanent snow, and another 0.7% is stored in groundwater, lakes, rivers, streams, and soil. Only a thousandth of 1% of the water on Earth exists as water vapor in the atmosphere. Figure 4.1 is a graphic representation of all the water on Earth.

Notice only about 2.5% of all the water on Earth is considered freshwater. The amount of freshwater on Earth is particularly important for humans. This water is not just for personal uses, but also for agriculture, livestock, and industrial uses. Freshwater exists in lakes, rivers, groundwater, and frozen as snow and ice. Estimates of groundwater are particularly difficult to make, and these estimates vary widely. One of the United States' most important natural resources is groundwater which is found in aquifers stored below the earth's surface. About 33% of the water that county and city water departments supply to households and businesses (public supply) comes from groundwater. Groundwater also provides drinking water for more than 90% of the rural population who do not get their water delivered to them from a county/city water department or from a private water company. According to the USGS, fresh groundwater withdrawal accounted for approximately 31% of all water used in Texas, most of which was used for irrigation. Some major cities, such as San Antonio, Texas, rely solely on groundwater for all their needs. As populations increase, the available sites for surface reservoirs will become more limited and the withdrawals of groundwater are expected to rise significantly. Figure 4.2 is a breakdown by the USGS for total water withdrawals of groundwater and surface water in 2005 (Mgal/d = millions of gallons per day).

Just like the interconnectedness of water in the hydrologic cycle, there is a direct correlation between surface water and groundwater. Water is stored on top as surface water and below the surface as groundwater. When water collects on the surface, it will runoff or soak into the ground.

Global Water Distribution

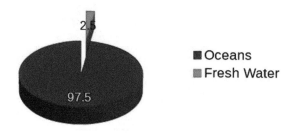

Fresh Water Distribution

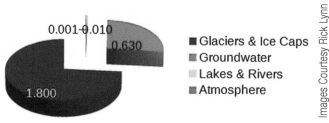

Figure 4.1 Breakdown of water on Earth.

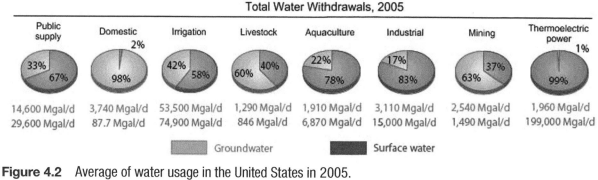

Figure 4.2 Average of water usage in the United States in 2005.

When water infiltrates the unsaturated zone of the sub-surface, gravity moves the water gradually downward into the saturated zone, becoming groundwater. The ground must be permeable, having the ability to move water and gasses through it, as well as have space between the particles of sediment, being porous. Saturated rock that is permeable and porous enough to allow easy movement of water is called an aquifer. The water table is the line between the saturated and unsaturated areas of sediment. Keep in mind the water table is typically not constant and will fluctuate within a transition zone throughout the seasons. If you are in a very arid or dry region, the water table will be very deep below the surface, whereas in wet areas the water table can be near or at the surface. The water table will fluctuate depending on how quickly the groundwater is recharged from surface water infiltration. The saturated zones of groundwater are where wells are drilled

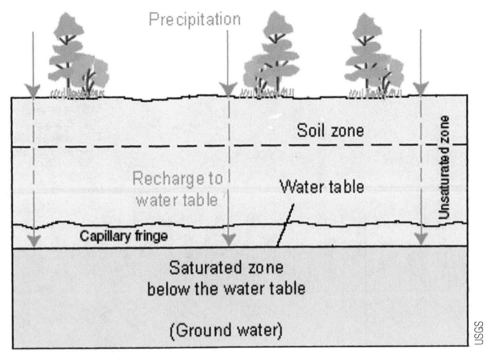

Figure 4.3   Groundwater of the subsurface.

to for water collection. Figure 4.3 gives a representation of the zones and water table. If water is being removed from a groundwater supply faster than it is able to recharge, the water table will drop. If the water table drops below the depth of a drilled well, the well becomes 'dry' and a new deeper well will need to be drilled.

Water is used much more than for personal use; it is also used for electricity and irrigation. One of the largest uses of water in the United States and the world is for the production of electrical power. Water is used to cool the power-producing equipment and used in generating electricity with steam-driven turbine generators. This is why you find large power-production facilities near sources of water such as lakes, rivers, and coastal regions. Irrigation is also a large contributor to the withdrawal of freshwater, especially in the United States. Figure 4.4 is a graphical representation by the USGS breaking down the categories of water use by state. Notice the two states with the highest usage are California and Texas.

So, where did all of this water come from?

The Earth did not start out with all this life-giving water. Scientists believe that in the early stages of Earth's development there was very little water and it was not on the surface due to extreme solar activity and lack of atmosphere; Earth was too hot for water to incorporate into a solid body. Early stages of Earth's development in the solar system show remarkable changes in water content. Scientists believe some of the Earth's water came from outgassing of volcanoes releasing water vapor into the atmosphere. This alone probably did not produce enough to form stable pools on the surface. More water was added to the planet during several hypothesized large impacts from asteroids from the outer asteroid belt. Comparison of isotope ratios found in water on Earth and water from comets and asteroids has revealed that the majority of the Earth's water comes from asteroids. However, the Earth is no longer receiving large quantities of water from these sources,

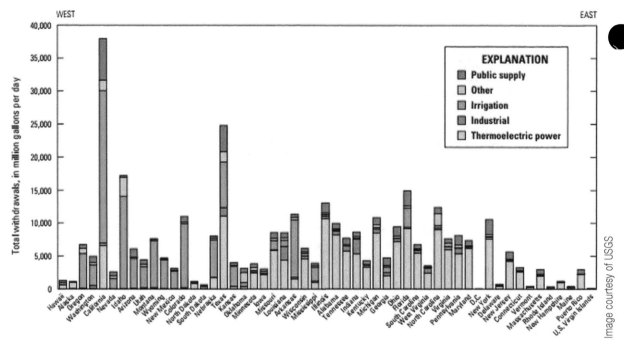

Figure 4.4   Total water withdrawals by State and bar chart showing categories by State from west to east, 2010.

and the water amounts on and in the planet do not fluctuate by a noticeable amount. This means that approximately the same amount of water has been here for billions of years and is continuously recycled through the hydrologic cycle. You are drinking the same water the dinosaurs drank!

Water, water, everywhere. . .

Freshwater available to humans is less than 2% of the total global supply, but what does this mean by location. In some parts of the world such as most of North America, the population is relatively 'lucky' in terms of availability. The infrastructure and abundant sources of water found in North America allow for a surplus where many people do not consider the impact or possibility of not having water. Water scarcity is either the lack of enough water (quantity) or lack of access to safe water (quality). Most of us would find it difficult to imagine the reality that clean, safe water is not something that is readily available everywhere on the planet and should not be taken for granted. In the developing world, finding a reliable source of safe water is often time consuming and expensive. This is known as economic scarcity. Water can be found, but it may require extensive resources to access which is not an economic option for some regions. In other areas, the lack of water is a more substantial problem. There simply is not enough. This is referred to as physical scarcity. There are many interpretations on water scarcity, and in some regions water resources are difficult to measure due to lack of available data. When looking at the map below from NASA's Soil Moisture Active Passive observatory (fig. 4.5), it is easy to visualize the regions of the world having problems with water resources. This leads to regions with little or no drop growth or resources for populations.

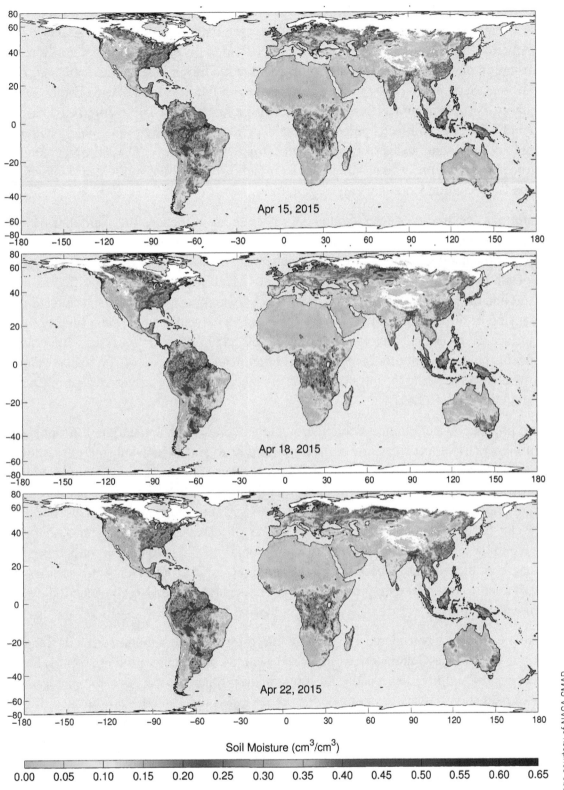

Soil Moisture (cm³/cm³)

Figure 4.5   Global Soil Moisture, April 2015.

In some areas, water availability is not the problem, but water quality is. In the United States, the Environmental Protection Agency (EPA) establishes regulations and provides guidance to states, Native American tribes, and U.S. territories. The EPA attempts to ensure that standards and other measures are in place to protect human health and aquatic life in lakes, rivers, streams, and other surface waters. Section 304(a)(1) of the Clean Water Act requires the EPA to develop criteria for water quality that accurately reflects the latest scientific knowledge. These criteria are based solely on data and scientific judgments on pollutant concentrations and environmental or human health effects giving maximum levels of contamination for a water supply. The EPA has a compliance and enforcement department to ensure that governments, businesses, and industry understand and follow the U.S. environmental laws and regulations.

There are many natural processes combined with human influences that can alter the physical and chemical composition of water. Natural processes would include the weathering of bedrock minerals and the natural leaching of organic matter and nutrients from the soil. This is part of the reason groundwater in aquifers typically seems so 'clean'; it is naturally purified as the water moves through the bedrock. Atmospheric processes of evapotranspiration (plants and animals) and the deposition of dust and salt by wind are other factors contributing to water quality, especially on the surface. Hydrological factors that lead to runoff and biological processes within the aquatic environment are also contributors and are susceptible to human influences. Typically, water quality is determined by comparing the physical and chemical characteristics of a water sample with water quality guidelines or standards.

The most prevalent water quality problem around the world is eutrophication. Eutrophication is a result of high-nutrient loads (mainly phosphorus and nitrogen), which substantially impairs beneficial uses of water. Agricultural runoff, domestic sewage (also a source of microbial pollution), and industrial effluents are all major nutrient sources in eutrophication. Atmospheric inputs from fossil fuel burning and bush fires also contribute to surface water nutrient loads. The relatively longer water residence times and complex dynamics of lakes and reservoirs make them particularly susceptible to the negative impacts of eutrophication. Their role as an integrating sink for pollutants from their drainage basins leads to increased input from other water sources. Human influences such as personal care products and pharmaceuticals are also considered a detrimental factor in water quality.

One example, and often considered the 'poster child' for water and sanitation crisis, is Bangladesh – a country in South Asia. Bangladesh exhibits both scarcity and quality problems with a high population of over 160 million and a naturally contaminated water source. As a comparison, the U.S. Census Bureau shows Texas has around 27.8 million, and the United States around 323 million people as of 2016. In Bangladesh, 97% of people have access to a water point through groundwater wells; however, the groundwater source is from alluvial and deltaic sediment deposits high in arseno pyrite, pyrite, iron sulfate, and iron oxide. These minerals dissolve naturally in the water creating an arsenic-rich water supply (fig. 4.6) which causes major health issues such as arsenic poisoning and arsenicosis.

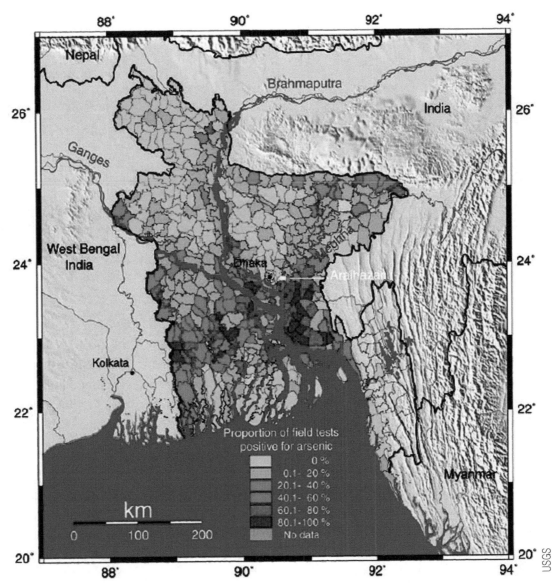

Figure 4.6   Arsenic levels in groundwater wells, Bangladesh (U.S. EPA standard is < 0.01ppm).

There are two main ways to contaminate groundwater. Point source pollution is where a specific location can be identified as the source. Scientists will use a contamination plume to locate the source of contamination. This can be done because water moves underground the way it moves above ground (down slope). Therefore, any particles carried in the water will disperse and dilute in the direction of flow. By sampling a possible contaminated region, a map can be drawn of contamination levels with the highest levels being closest to the source. An example would be a leaking fuel tank or landfill; this would be considered point source pollution. When an oil pipeline leaks (Figure 4.7), the oil can seep into groundwater and flow underground. The contamination plume will flow away from the source until natural processes break the oil down further from the source.

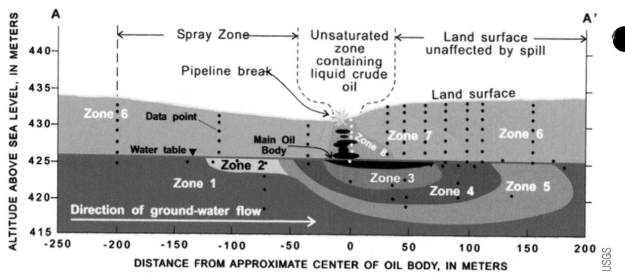

Figure 4.7 Contamination plume in groundwater.

A non-point source would be when contaminates are distributed over a large area, such as pesticides sprayed on agricultural crops. Contaminants must often be removed from groundwater before it reaches wells used by agriculture and municipal water systems. The removal and containment of pollutants are called remediation. This is accomplished easier in areas where remediation processes are readily available and water quality standards are enforced. Remediation is required when concentrations of contaminants exceed or are expected to exceed predetermined levels for the type of resource that is impacted. For example, lead levels in drinking water should not exceed the EPA action level of 0.015 mg/L.

The first step in remediation is removal of the source of contamination if possible. There are several types of remediation methods some of which are very expensive and sometimes ineffective. Two main types of remediation are chemical remediation and bioremediation. Chemical remediation is when chemical compounds are delivered in the subsurface to destroy (typically converted to water and carbon dioxide or to nontoxic substances) the organic molecules. Bioremediation involves the use of microorganisms for the breakdown of carbon-based contaminants by microbial organisms into smaller compounds. The microbial organisms transform the contaminants through metabolic or enzymatic processes. Bioremediation processes vary greatly, but frequently the final product of the remediation is carbon dioxide or methane. Bioremediation is a key process in the natural attenuation of contaminants at hazardous waste sites. Another type of remediation called phytoremediation can be very effective for heavy metals and metal-like elements, but it can only be utilized in areas where the ground water is close to the surface. This remediation consists of growing certain plants so their roots tap the groundwater. The plants accumulate the toxins as they grow, then the plants are harvested and discarded.

Other Problems with Groundwater Removal

Groundwater is a valuable resource both in the United States and throughout the world. Where surface water, such as lakes and rivers, are scarce or inaccessible, groundwater supplies many of the hydrologic needs of people. It is the source of drinking water for about half of the total population

Figure 4.8   Popular image of 1981 Winter Park, FL sinkhole.

and nearly all of the rural population, and it provides over 50 billion gallons per day for agricultural needs. Groundwater depletion caused by sustained groundwater pumping is a key issue associated with groundwater use and some results are:

- Lowering of the Water Table – this can result in dry wells

- Reduction of Water in Streams and Lakes – alteration of water movement between aquifers and streams, lakes, or wetlands by intercepting surface discharges or increasing movement of surface water into aquifers

- Land Subsidence – loss of support below the ground, soil collapses, compacts, and drops

- Deterioration of water quality – saltwater intrusion; excessive pumping near saline sources (ocean) can cause saltwater to migrate inland and upward, resulting in saltwater contamination of the water supply

There have been many incidents identified recently with subsidence and groundwater removal, such as sink holes being created in numerous places around the United States (fig. 4.8).

Denison Water and Water Usage

Groundwater is a key source for Texas, providing 60% of the water used in the state. In the Sherman-Denison area, the major and minor aquifers that provide water to Grayson County wells are the Trinity and Woodbine aquifers. The east and central sections of Sherman receive groundwater, North and West Sherman gets lake water, and the industrial area to the south of town is equipped to receive both. A Texas Water Development Board (TWDB) report on 2010–2011 groundwater conditions showed monitoring wells in North Central Texas' Trinity Aquifer recorded a median drop in water levels of 8.5 feet and an average decline of 12 feet between 2010 and 2011. In the Woodbine Aquifer, which is tracked by only one monitoring well in Denison, the water level declined by 18.9 feet from 2010 to 2011 (statistics from the TWDB).

Another source of water in the region is surface water from Lake Texoma, which serves as a water source for the surrounding counties. One concern for using surface water for an area is drought conditions creating demand outweighing supply with increasing populations. There are many water right-holders issued to Lake Texoma which include the surrounding areas, Oklahoma, and even an authorization to divert water to Lake Lavon. While there are a number of other factors at play, if the maximum amount of water available for water storage was removed by the rights-holders during a single year, it would amount to an approximate drop in lake levels of three feet over the entire year. Water is also lost from evaporation especially for shallow lakes with a large surface area. The amount lost by Lake Texoma simply to evaporation was estimated to be nearly six feet in 2012.

Water conservation is an important concept in all areas, even those rich in supply. There are many factors which can affect a water supply such as over-use, drought, and contamination. Consider how much water you use. What steps could be taken to minimize a population's impact on its water supply?

Lab 5

Earthquakes

One of the most difficult problems faced by Earth scientists is determining the physical properties of Earth's interior. Seismology is a branch of Earth science that combines mathematics and physics to explain the nature of earthquakes and how they can be used to gather information about Earth beyond our view. Investigation of seismic waves and knowledge of how various waves move through different materials have given scientists an insight into what lies beneath the surface.

Earthquakes are vibrations of Earth that occur when the rigid materials of the lithosphere are strained beyond their limit, yield or fracture, and 'spring back' to their original shape, rapidly releasing stored energy. Earthquakes occur when underground rocks suddenly release built-up stress. Rocks respond most commonly by shifting position along pre-existing faults, either vertically or laterally, or in some cases, by breaking and creating new faults. This released energy radiates in all directions from the source of the earthquake (below the surface) called the focus. The focus of most earthquakes is from 5 to 60 kilometers deep. The point located on the surface of the Earth directly above the focus is called the epicenter.

The energy is released in the form of seismic waves. Seismograph instruments are used to amplify and record the ground motions produced by passing seismic waves on seismograms (fig. 5.1).

When an earthquake occurs, seismograph stations throughout the world record the vibrations. Earthquakes transmit several types of energy waves. P-waves or primary waves are the fastest, and are the first to arrive at any seismograph station. These are followed by the S-waves or secondary waves. Because of the velocity difference, the seismogram will record the arrival of the P-wave first. At a later period of time, the seismogram will record the S-wave arrival. On a seismogram (the earthquake recorded by the seismograph), the difference in arrival times between P-waves and S-waves is pronounced and is easy to determine. With this information, you can calculate the distance between the earthquake epicenter and the seismograph. There are also other waves associated with earthquakes; these are called surface waves because they travel only near the surface of the Earth. They travel slower than either the P or the S waves, and so they arrive later than either the P or the S wave on a seismogram.

The lag time between the P and S waves is calculated by using the difference, in seconds, between the arrival of the P wave and the arrival of the S wave (fig. 5.2). To calculate the distance from the seismograph station to the epicenter, determine the lag time between the P and S waves by looking at the seismogram then use the P-S Wave Travel Time Curve (fig. 5.3) to find the distance.

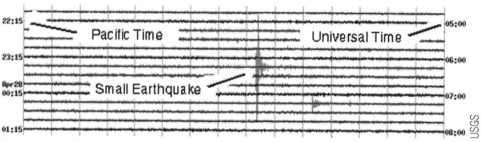

Figure 5.1   Drum seismographs and seismogram (printout) used by USGS.

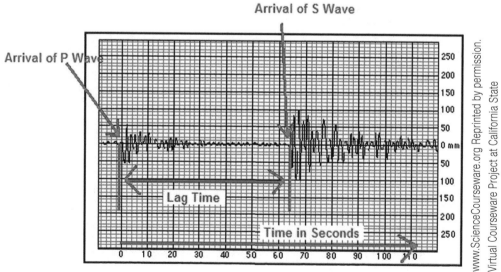

Figure 5.2   The first step to determine the location of epicenter is to find the lag time between the P and S wave arrival by looking at the seismogram.

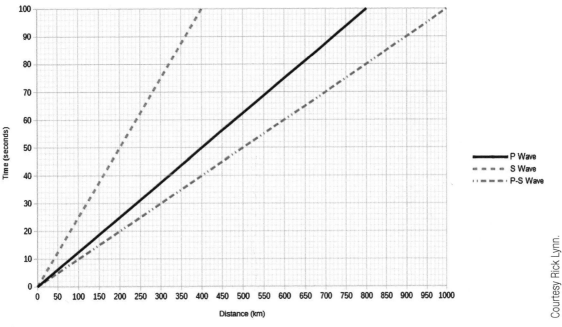

Figure 5.3   Travel-time curve for P, S and P-S wave lag time.

In figure 5.2, the time lag between the arrival of the P and S waves is approximately 64 seconds. By locating the place on the seismogram (fig. 5.2) where the P wave begins (in this case at time '0') then locating the time when the S wave arrives (in this case 64 seconds) you can determine the time lag between the arrival of the P wave and the arrival of the S wave (S – P = Lag, 64 – 0 = 64 sec). It is very important when reading the seismograms to pay attention to the value of the lines and units. On this particular seismogram, you will notice that each line on the x-axis (bottom) for time represents an increment of 2 seconds, and y-axis (vertical) for amplitude represents an increment of 10 mm.

Next a Travel-Time Curve is used to determine the distance from the seismograph station to the epicenter of the earthquake. A travel-time curve (fig. 5.3) is a graph of the time that it takes for seismic waves to travel from the epicenter of an earthquake to seismograph stations varying distances away. The curves are the result of analyzing seismic waves from thousands of earthquakes, received by hundreds of seismic stations around the world. They are used by seismologists to quickly locate earthquakes.

The upper curve shows the S wave travel time graphed versus distance, the center one shows the P wave travel time versus distance, and the lower one shows the variation in distance with the difference of the S and P travel times (the lag time versus distance). Again, make sure you pay attention to the units and increments represented by the lines. For the seismogram in Figure 5.2, the determined lag time was 64 seconds, so the distance can be determined by finding the time on the y-axis (vertical), go over to line that represents the S-P lag time then extrapolate down to find the distance (fig. 5.4). For this example from the seismogram above, the distance is 630 km.

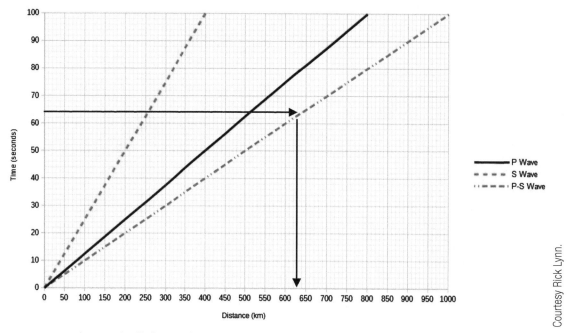

Figure 5.4 Locate the P-S wave lag time on the Y axis then move to the right along that line until you reach the P-S wave lag time curve. Then move straight down to the X axis to determine the distance to the epicenter.

Triangulation

With one station we can locate how far away an earthquake happened from that seismograph station, and with three stations we can actually pinpoint more or less the epicenter of the earthquake (i.e. where the earthquake would appear on the surface). It works on the following manner:

Step 1

For our purpose, let's say an earthquake happened 10 kilometers away from one specific station. We can now draw a circle around that station that is exactly 10 kilometers from the center. So we now know that the earthquake happened somewhere on that circle.

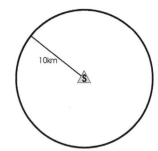

Step 2

Now let's look at another station. We measure the P and S-waves to find out that the earthquake happened 5 kilometers from this station. So we do the same thing and draw a circle around that station that is exactly 5 kilometers from the center. If we did things right, the two circles should intersect at two points. We can now deduce that the earthquake happened on one of the two places where the circles intersect.

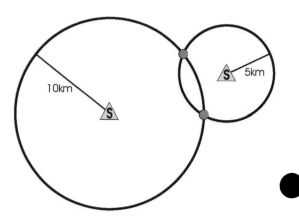

Step 3

Now we take a third station and again do the same thing. Let's say the earthquake falls 8 kilometers away from that station. Again, we draw the circle 8 kilometers away from the station. Now, if we did this right, the three circles should intersect at one point. This point represents the epicenter of the earthquake. The more stations used, the more accurately its location and size can be determined.

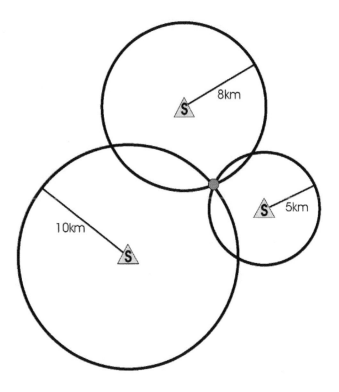

Determining the Magnitude of the Earthquake

Earthquake magnitude is reported using the Richter Magnitude Scale. The Richter Scale indicates the amount of ground movement and energy released during the earthquake. This is a logarithmic scale; therefore going from 3 to 4 on the scale represents 10 times the amount of ground movement caused by the earthquake. However, going from 3 to 4 on the scale represents 30 times the amount of energy released during the earthquake. Earthquakes with magnitudes from 1 to 3 are minor and hardly ever felt. Earthquakes with magnitudes of 4 to 6 are moderate and can cause some damage to structures. Earthquakes with magnitudes greater than 7 are considered major, and can do tremendous damage. To determine the Richter magnitude, the distance from the epicenter and amplitude of the largest seismic wave must be known. The largest seismic wave amplitude is measured from the centerline of the seismogram to the maximum point of the largest wave (fig. 5.5).

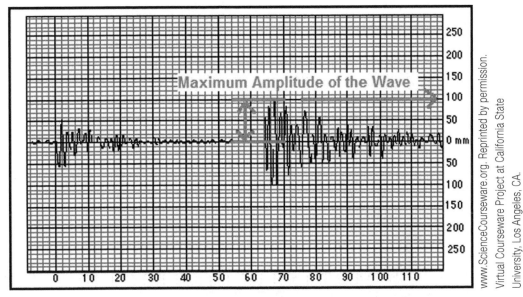

Figure 5.5 Amplitude measured on Seismogram, in this case amplitude = 100 mm.

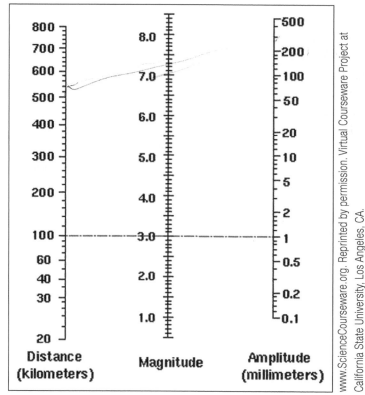

Figure 5.6   Richter Nomogram used to determine the magnitude of an earthquake.

To determine the earthquake magnitude, a Richter Nomogram (fig. 5.6) is used which correlates distance from the epicenter (which was determined to be 630 km from the seismogram used earlier) and amplitude from the same seismograph station to determine the magnitude. Plot the distance to the epicenter on the distance line (630 km) and the amplitude on the amplitude line (100 mm) then draw a line between those two points (fig. 5.7). The magnitude of the earthquake is the point on the magnitude scale where the line crosses. In this example, the epicenter is 630 km from the seismograph station and the amplitude of the largest wave is 100 mm. Therefore, the magnitude of the earthquake is approximately 7.1.

When did the earthquake occur?

After the distance from the epicenter to a seismograph station has been calculated, the exact time the earthquake began can be ascertained. Using the seismogram information from Figure 5.2, the distance to the epicenter was estimated at 630 km. The travel-time curve can be used to determine the length of time required for the P wave to arrive at the recording station. In this example, the time is approximately 78 seconds (fig. 5.8). If the seismogram recorded the first P wave at 9:10:40AM (hours:minutes:seconds) and the travel time for the P wave was 78 seconds, the time the earthquake began is 9:09:22 AM. By subtracting the 78 second travel time from the time of arrival of the P Wave (9:10:40 AM), the exact time the earthquake began is known.

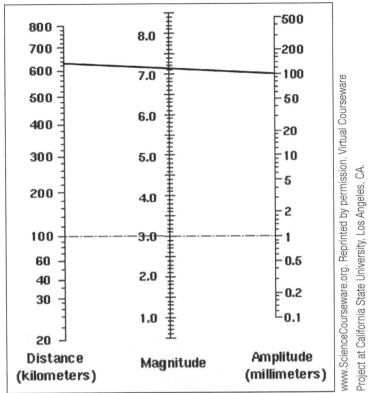

Figure 5.7   In order to determine the magnitude of the earthquake, draw a line from the distance live on the left to the amplitude line on the right. Where the line intersects the magnitude line in the middle tells the magnitude of the earthquake. For our example, the magnitude is a 7.1.

www.ScienceCourseware.org. Reprinted by permission. Virtual Courseware Project at California State University, Los Angeles, CA.

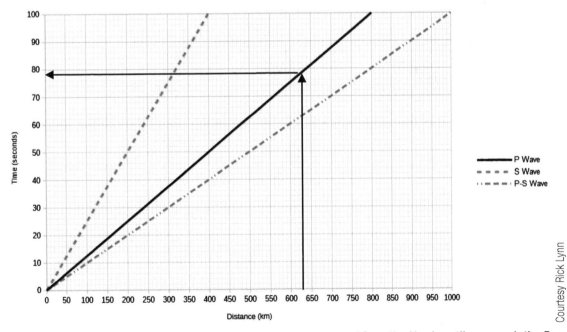

Courtesy Rick Lynn

Figure 5.8   Using the distance from the epicenter, move upward from the X axis until you reach the P wave travel curve. Then move to the left until you intersect the Y axis to determine the length of time required for the P wave to travel from the epicenter to the seismic station.

Using Seismic Waves to Study the Interior

Seismic waves are divided into two types: body waves and surface waves. Body waves include P and S waves, and these are the two types of waves that are used to determine the internal structure of the Earth. P waves (pressure or primary waves) travel as a region of compression. A longitudinal P wave has the ability to move through solid rock and fluid rock, like water or the semi-liquid layers of the earth. It pushes and pulls the rock it moves through in the same way sound waves push and pull the air. S waves are known as shear waves, and their motion is perpendicular to the direction of travel (like waves created when shaking a rope). S waves cannot move through a liquid or gas. This is because a liquid is not rigid enough to transmit an S wave. Waves can reflect off (bounce off) of materials that have a different density, or they can be refracted (bent) as they pass through a boundary between layers of different material. Scientists use the difference in arrival times of reflected and refracted waves from distant earthquakes to construct a picture of what the Earth's interior looks like (fig. 5.9).

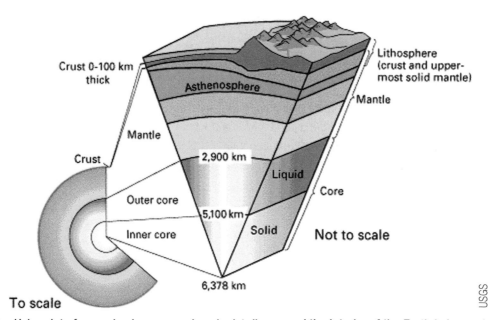

Figure 5.9   Using data from seismic waves seismologist discovered the interior of the Earth is layered.

Coordinate Systems, Maps & Time Zones

Globes and maps each have a system of north-south and east-west lines called the Earth's grid, that forms the basis for locating points on Earth. The grid is much like a large sheet of graph paper that has been laid over the surface of Earth. Using the system is very similar to using a graph in that the position of a point is determined by the intersection of two lines.

Longitude

Longitude is an angular measure either East or West of the Prime Meridian. Longitude lines (also called meridians) start at the North pole and extend to the South pole. When measuring longitude, the maximum angle East or West is 180°. The Prime Meridian divides the earth into an Eastern and Western Hemisphere. When viewing the earth from a perspective from above the North Geographic Pole (fig. 6.1), the Western Hemisphere is clockwise from the Prime Meridian to the 180th meridian. The Eastern Hemisphere is counterclockwise from the Prime Meridian to the 180th meridian. Meridians run north and south.

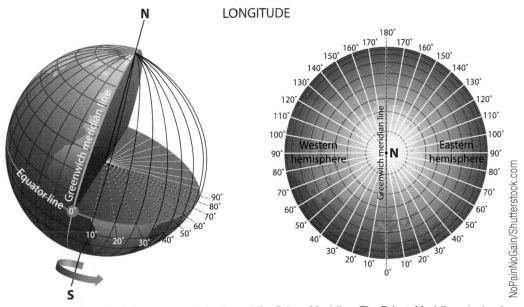

Figure 6.1 Longitude is measured starting at the Prime Meridian. The Prime Meridian starts at the North Pole and extends to the South Pole and goes through Greenwich, England. The Prime Meridian is also known as the Greenwich Meridian Line.

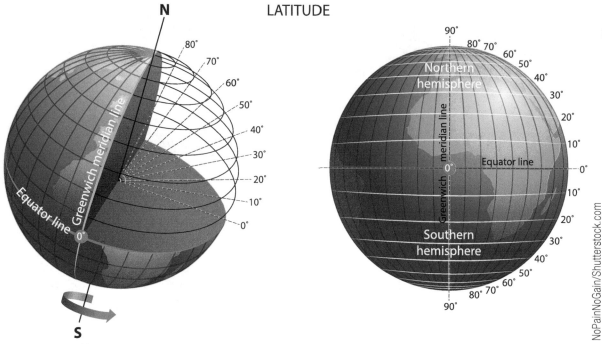

LATITUDE

Figure 6.2 Lines of latitude are parallel to the equator and extend East-West. The equator divides the Earth into northern and southern hemispheres. The intersection of a parallel of latitude with a meridian of longitude determines the location of a point on Earth's surface.

Latitude

Latitude is an angle either North or South of the equator (fig. 6.2). The equator is 0° latitude. The equator divides the earth into a Northern and Southern Hemisphere. Thus, if the latitude of a location is 30 degrees north latitude, that location is 30° of arc from the equator and in the Northern Hemisphere. Latitude is always expressed as either North or South. The largest possible angle of latitude is 90°. Latitude is expressed on the globe by parallel lines North and South of the equator that form circles around the Earth. The parallels are oriented East-West and measure angles North or South of the equator. The equator is the only parallel of latitude that divides the earth in to two equal parts or hemispheres. On the globe, parallels of latitude intersect meridians of longitude at 90° angles.

Angular Measurements

Earth's shape is nearly spherical. Since parallels and meridians mark distances on a sphere, there designation, like distance around a circle, is given in degrees. Latitude and longitude are angular measures and are expressed in degrees of arc. There are 60 minutes (denoted by a′) in one degree and 60 seconds (denoted by a″) in one minute. Thus 15° and 14° 60' are the same thing since 60' equals one degree. The type of map or globe determines the accuracy to which a place may be located. On detailed maps, it is possible to estimate latitude and longitude to the nearest degree, minute, and second. On a world map or globe, it may only be possible to estimate to the nearest whole degree or two. Today most ships use GPS (global positioning system) navigational satellites to determine location. Early explorers had to use visual observations, be aware of the concept of latitude, and could use the angle of the North Star (Polaris) above the horizon to determine their north-south position in the northern hemisphere. For example, if standing at the North Pole one would look overhead (90 degrees above the horizon) to see Polaris. Their latitude would be approximately 90 degrees North. If standing on the Equator (0 degrees latitude), they would observe Polaris on the horizon (0 degree angle above the horizon).

Longitude and Time

Time, while independent of latitude, is very much related to longitude. Time on Earth can be kept in two ways. Solar or Sun time uses the position of the Sun in the sky to determine time. Standard time, the system used throughout most of the world, divides the globe into 24 standard time zones.

Solar time is used to determine longitude, but certain basic rules are important:

- Earth rotates on its axis from west to east (eastward) or counterclockwise when viewed from above the North Pole

- It is noon, Sun time, on the meridian that is directly facing the Sun (the Sun has reached its highest position in the sky, called the zenith) and midnight on the meridian on the opposite side of Earth.

- The time interval from one noon by the Sun to the next noon averages 24 hours and is known as the mean solar day.

- Earth turns through 360 degrees of longitude in one mean solar day, which is equivalent to 15 degrees of longitude per hour or 1 degree of longitude every 4 minutes of time.

- Places that are east or west of each other, regardless of distance, have different solar times. For example, people located to the east of the noon meridian have already experienced noon; their time is afternoon [p.m. – post (after) meridiem (the noon meridian)]. People located west of the noon meridian have yet to reach noon; their time is a.m. (ante meridiem). Time becomes later going eastward and earlier going westward.

Accurate clocks called chronometers are still carried by ships as a backup system. The shipboard chronometer is set to keep the time at a known place on Earth, for example the Prime Meridian. If it is noon by the Sun where the ship is located and at that same instant the chronometer indicates that it is 8 a.m. on the Prime meridian, the ship must be 60 degrees longitude east of the Prime Meridian (4 hours difference X 15 degrees per hour, and east because the ship's time is later than the Prime Meridian).

Standard Time is used by most of the world and is divided into 24 time zones. The Earth rotates 15 degrees of longitude for each hour of time that passes. Therefore, the Earth is divided into 24 time zones centering on the Prime Meridian. Each time zone is then centered on a longitude line every 15° moving east and west from the Prime Meridian. The Central time zone (where we live) is centered on the 90°W longitude line (fig. 6.3).

There is one hour of difference in time between each time zone. Time zones do not always follow longitude lines exactly; there are deviations for convenience sake. The continental United States is covered by four time zones: the Eastern, Central, Mountain, and Pacific (fig. 6.4).

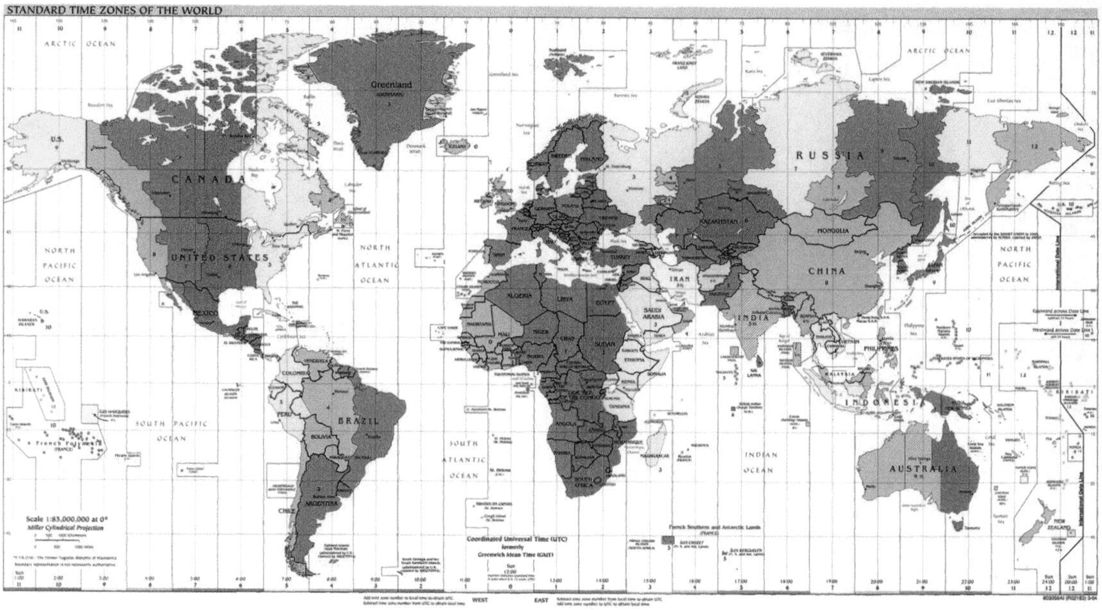

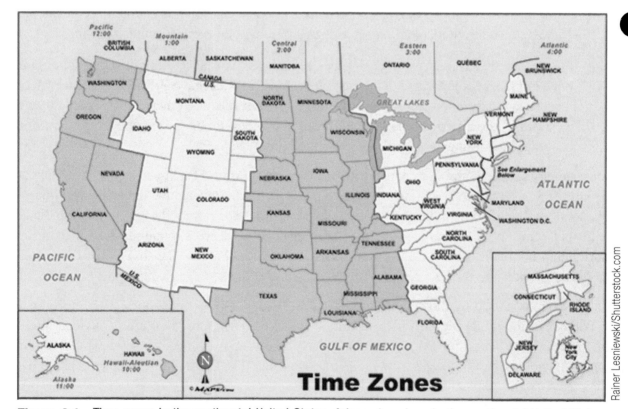

Figure 6.3 This is a world time zone map. There are 24 time zones that are 15° wide. Each one is centered on a meridian that is a multiple of 15°.

Taken from the Library of Congress, https://www.loc.gov/resource/g3201b.ct001302/

Rainer Lesniewski/Shutterstock.com

Figure 6.4 Time zones in the continental United States. Arizona is unique in the continental United States, because it does not observe Daylight Saving Time.

To determine the time in a time zone east of your location add 1 hour for each time zone. To determine the time in a time zone west of your location subtract one hour for each time zone. If the difference in longitude between two points is known, the time difference can also be calculated. Remember, each time zone is 15° wide. If there is a longitudinal difference of 60° between two locations, then there are 4 time zones (60/15=4) separating them and thus four hours (1 hour for each time zone) separating the two locations. For example, London is in the time zone centered on the Prime Meridian. The Central time zone in the United States is centered on the 90°W longitude line. So there is 90° difference in longitude between the two time zones. Since each time zone is 15° wide, there is a 6-hour difference (90/15=6) between London and the Central time zone in the United States. This information can then be used to determine the time in London based on the time in the Central time zone. Moving east, hours are added as we cross each time zone. If the current time in the Central time zone is 2:00PM we need to add six hours to the time to determine the time in London. Therefore, the time in London is 8:00 PM.

Honolulu is in the time zone centered on the 150°W meridian. There is 60° difference between the Central time zone (90°W) and Honolulu which means there is a 4-hour time difference. Because we are moving west from the Central time zone to Honolulu, hours are subtracted for each time zone that is crossed. If the current time in the Central Time zone is 2:00 PM, four hours are subtracted to determine the time in Honolulu. Therefore, the time in Honolulu would be 10:00 AM.

International Date Line

The **International Date Line** (fig. 6.3) is a line running from the North to the South Pole very near the 180th meridian. The International Date Line (IDL) defines where a new day on Earth begins. The time difference from the east to the west side of the IDL is 24 hours. When moving from east to west crossing the IDL, you must add 24 hours (one day) to the time. Moving from west to east across the IDL, you must subtract 24 hours from the time. For example, if it is 1:30 PM Friday, March 9th, on the east side of the IDL then it is 1:30 PM Saturday, March 10th, on the west side of the IDL.

Traveling from Honolulu to Sydney, Australia you cross four time zones because Honolulu is in the time zone centered at 150°W and Sydney is in the time zone based on 150°E; therefore, there is 60° of longitude between the two cities (60/15=4). If you leave Honolulu at 10:00 AM on Saturday on an 8-hour flight to Sydney what time will you arrive in Sydney? Because we are moving west, subtract the 4 hours from your departure time in Honolulu to determine the time in Sydney (10:00 AM - 4 hours = 6:00 AM). Now add 8 hours for your travel time (6:00 AM + 8 hours = 2:00PM). Now add one day (24 hours) to the arrival time because you crossed the IDL moving west and you arrive in Sydney at 2:00 PM Sunday afternoon.

Universal Transverse Mercator System

Another method being used for mapping is the **Universal Transverse Mercator System** or UTM for short. This is the default coordinate system used by most global positioning system (GPS) units. This system is based on 60 north-south zones that are each 6° wide. Each zone is numbered from west to east starting at the International Date Line. Each zone has its origin at the equator and a central meridian (fig. 6.5). The UTM zones for the United States are shown in figure 6.6.

UTM ZONE NUMBERS

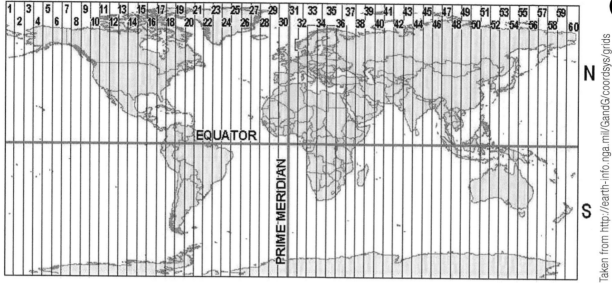

Figure 6.5   The UTM zones numbers and designators worldwide. The east-west 0 line is the equator.

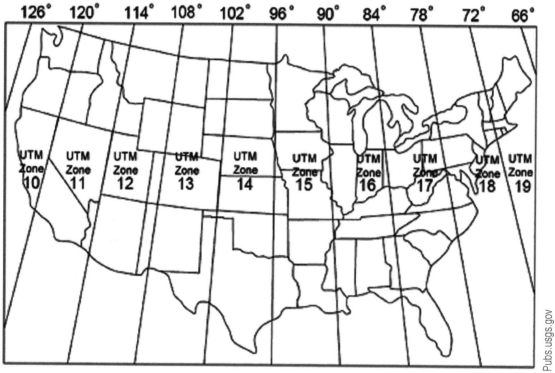

Figure 6.6   UTM Zones for the United States.

From the origin of each zone, a grid system is defined with lines intersecting at right angles. The east-west lines, moving north from the equator, are measured in meters. The north-south lines are measured from a false origin of 0 mE (meters east) that begins 500,000 meters west of the true origin. Remember the true origin is at the intersection of the equator and a central meridian line (fig. 6.5).

Types of Maps

There are several types of maps in use today. A road map shows roads, political boundaries, cities, and natural features like rivers & lakes. A topographic map shows topography and may include things like roads, dams, political boundaries, and buildings. **Topography** is the 3-dimensional shape of a surface. Therefore, topographic maps show changes in topography and elevation (3D information) on a 2D surface. Geological maps provide information about the types of rocks which are exposed at the surface and may include many of the same features as seen on topographic maps. Land use maps combine information from topographic, geologic, and soil maps to provide information about areas of potential flooding, landslides, areas sensitive to earthquakes, soil condition, locations impacted by hazardous waste, or ecologically sensitive areas.

Topographic Maps

Topographic maps are used not only by geologists but also anyone who enjoys the outdoors. Hikers, hunters, and backwoods campers all benefit from having access to topographic maps. These individuals use topographic maps to help locate and guide them on the Earth's surface. While modern technology, such as GPS systems, are great, nothing beats a good map when you are 30 km from nowhere! A topographic map is a representation of a 3-dimensional surface in two dimensions.

In the United States, topographic maps are published by the United States Geologic Survey (USGS). The maps are based on quadrangles. A quadrangle is a portion of the Earth's surface bounded by latitude and longitude lines. There are two common sizes of these maps: the 15 minute and 7½ minute topographic maps (remember there are 60 minutes in one degree). However, the 15 minute maps are being phased out and replaced with 30' x 60' maps.

The 15-minute map covers an area 15 minutes east to west and 15 minutes north to south. The 7½-minute map covers an area 7½ minutes east to west and 7½ minutes north to south. It takes four 7½ minute maps to make one 15-minute map. In order to cover 1° east to west and 1° north to south requires sixteen 15-minute quadrangle maps. The top of each map points to true geographic north. Because the magnetic poles wander slowly through time, geographic north and magnetic north are not the same. The difference between geographic and magnetic north is called the magnetic declination. There is a symbol on the bottom of each map showing the magnetic declination for the map at the time when it was produced (fig. 6.7).

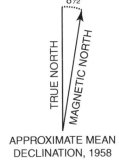

Figure 6.7   Example of magnetic declination symbol on a map.

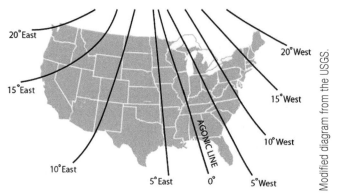

Figure 6.8 Magnetic declination map for the continental United States. In this area of Texas, the magnetic declination is about 6° east. The agonic line represents 0° declination.

The map date is important because the magnetic declination changes as the magnetic poles wander. Magnetic declination varies depending on your exact location on the planet also (fig. 6.8). In order to properly use a compass for navigation, magnetic declination must be corrected for, and maps indicate the correction that is required between magnetic and geographic north.

Contour Lines on Topographic Maps

Contour lines show points of equal elevation on a map. By utilizing contour lines, topographic maps are able to show relief (the topographic variation) of a land surface. Therefore, topographic maps show both elevation and topography. Features such as rivers, roads, buildings, and place names are included on topographic maps like they are on planimetric (2D) maps. A contour line is an imaginary line on the surface of the Earth that connects points of equal elevation. All points on a contour line have the same elevation. Elevation is a measure of the vertical distance between a point and a fixed datum. The datum is a fixed point of reference and is based on mean or average sea level. Therefore, sea level always has an elevation of 0. Contour lines have several characteristics :

1. Every point on a counter line has the same elevation.

2. Contour lines never cross each other nor do they converge or diverge. In very steep areas, it may appear that contour lines converge because they are so close together they get printed on top of each other.

3. Slopes rise or fall at right angles to contour lines. If the contour lines are evenly spaced, the slope is uniform. Contour lines that are spaced very close together indicate a steep slope while widely spaced contour lines indicate a gentle slope. If the contour lines are unevenly spaced, the slope is irregular.

4. Contour lines will encircle a hilltop, with the highest peak being within the innermost contour line. The highest elevation of the peak will normally be marked with an X and the elevation noted on the map.

5. Near the top of a ridge or within a valley, contour lines will occur in pairs. The pairs will be across the ridge line or valley.

6. When contour lines cross a stream, they bend upstream. This is called the Rule of V's (fig. 6.9). Therefore, the stream is flowing in the opposite direction of the bend in the contour lines.

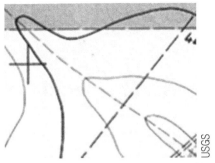

Figure 6.9   The dashed line running from the upper left to the lower right in this map section is a stream. Note how the contour lines bend as they cross the stream. The bend in a counter line points upstream. This is called the Rule of V's.

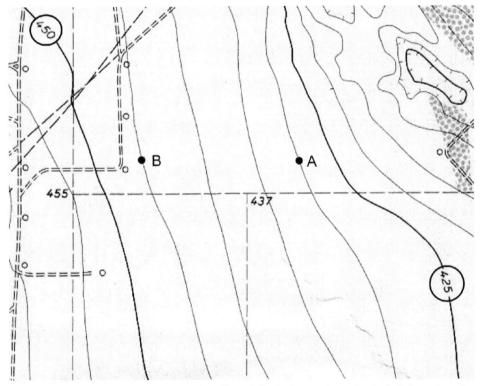

Figure 6.10   In this example, the elevation of the index contours is circled. Based on the difference in elevation between the index contours, the contour interval is 5 feet.

Contour intervals are the amount of elevation change between each contour line. This will vary depending on the topography of the area being mapped. If the contour interval is 20 feet, each contour line represents 20 feet of elevation change on the map. For an example of contour lines and contour intervals, see figure 6.10.

On contour maps, every fifth contour line is an index contour. These contour lines are drawn heavier and have the elevation marked on them. In figure 6.10, the elevation of the index contours is circled. The contour interval for this map is 5 feet. Using this information, the elevation of point A and B can be ascertained. Starting at the lowest index contour (425 feet), the elevation of point A is

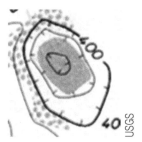

Figure 6.11   The first contour line with hatch marks repeats the last elevation (400 feet in this example), the depression contours within that indicate lower elevation. If we assume a contour interval of 20 feet, the second depression contour would be at an elevation of 380 feet and the third depression contour would be at an elevation of 360 feet.

430 feet because it is the next contour line on the map (425 feet [index contour] + 5 feet [contour interval]=430 feet). The elevation of the point labeled B is 445 feet. The difference in elevation between point A and point B is 15 feet.

Depression contours are closed contour lines with hatches pointing to a lower elevation. The first contour line of depression contours always repeats the elevation of the last contour line that was crossed. Other depression contours represent lower elevations within the circle (fig. 6.11). Each depression contour, after the first one, indicates a decrease in elevation by the amount of the contour interval.

Map Scale

A map scale allows the user of the map to determine the size of the area covered by the map and ascertain the distance between different points on the map. Three maps scales are commonly used. The ratio or fractional scale represents a ratio between a distance on the map and the actual distance on the ground (fig. 6.12). In this example, the fractional scale is 1:24,000. This means that 1 unit measured on the map (typically inches or centimeters) represents 24,000 units on the ground. If the ratio scale is in inches and you measure 1 inch between points on the map the actual distance between those points on the surface of the Earth is 24,000 inches. A common ratio scale used by the USGS is 1:62,500 inches. With that scale, one inch on the ground is approximately 1 mile on the map.

A graphic scale is a line or bar subdivided into divisions corresponding to a kilometer or mile (fig. 6.12). These graphic lines are subdivided into smaller units to allow for more precise measurements. The smaller divisions on the graphic scale are normally done to the left of zero. This scale is easy to visualize and will stay in proper proportion if the map is reduced or enlarged.

To determine distance on a map using the graphic scale, use a ruler to measure the length of the graphic scale from 0 to 1 (you can use either the mile or kilometer scale). Now measure the distance on the map between two points, and divide the length representing the distance between those points by the length of the graphic scale to determine the distance in miles or kilometers between the two points on the map (fig. 6.13). In this example, the graphic scale for 1 kilometer is 4.1 centimeters (cm) in length. The measured length on the map between two points is 8.4 cm (see the dashed line in fig. 6.14). Now divide the measured length between the two map points

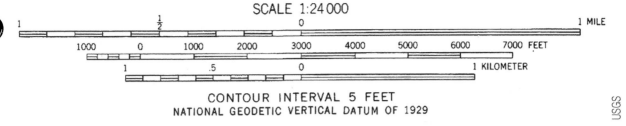

CONTOUR INTERVAL 5 FEET
NATIONAL GEODETIC VERTICAL DATUM OF 1929

USGS

Figure 6.12 A typical set of scales used on topographic maps. The one at the top is the ratio or fractional scale. The three scales below the fractional scale are all graphic scales. The contour interval will also be included with the map scales.

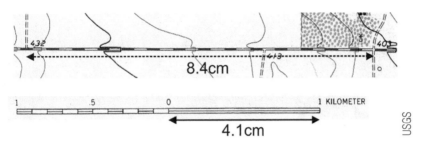

USGS

Figure 6.13 This example uses the graphic scale to determine the distance between two points on a topographic map.

by the length that represents 1 km on the graphic scale (8.4/4.1). The result of the division is 2.05 which means there are 2.05 km between the two points on the map represented by the dashed line in figure 6.13.

Verbal scales are rarely written on maps but are used to discuss maps. A common example would be "one inch equals one mile." This means that if you measure one inch on the map using a ruler, the actual distance on the ground would be one mile. The fractional scale 1:62,500 is close to the verbal scale of one inch equals one mile because there are 63,360 inches in one mile (5,280 feet * 12 inches per foot = 63,360 inches). Converting verbal scales to fractional scales is much easier with maps that use the metric system for the scale. For example, fractional scales of 1:50,000, 1:100,000, and 1:250,000 mean that one centimeter on the map represents 0.5, 1.0, and 2.5 km, respectively (as maps are updated, the USGS is switching to a metric scale).

The scale used on a map will vary depending on the size of the area to be displayed. A scale of 1:12,000 (1 inch equals 1,000 feet on the ground) may be suitable for a map of a small city but would be unrealistic for a map of the state of Texas.

Bearings

The direction from one point to another on Earth is called a bearing. Bearings are measured in degrees, but there are two ways to state the bearing. Quadrant bearings measure the bearing as a number of degrees east or west of north or south (fig. 6.14). Azimuth bearings measure the number of degrees on a 360° circle (fig. 6.15). When using azimuth bearings north is 0 and 360°, east is 90°, south is 180°, and west is 270°.

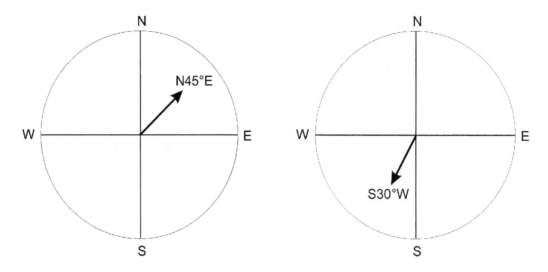

Figure 6.14 Using quadrant bearings, measurements start from North or South and an East or West component is added. The example on the left is pointing northeast and is read north 45° east. The example on the right would be read south 30° west meaning the arrow is pointing 30° west of south.

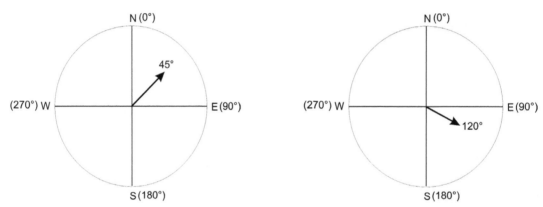

Figure 6.15 This figure uses azimuth bearings. There are 90° between each of the major compass directions. The arrow in the example on the left is pointing at 45° which is the same as northeast or in quadrant bearing, N45°E. The example on the right is 120° which in quadrant bearings is S60°E.

Public Land Survey

The **Public Land Survey** began in the late 1700s. With the exception of the 13 original states, surveys were made of one or more **base lines**, which run east-west and one or more **principle meridians**, which run north-south. After these lines were surveyed, additional lines were surveyed at 6-mile intervals from these lines. This creates a grid of squares 6 miles on each side (fig. 6.16).

Each square moving east and west from the principal meridian is called a **township** whereas the squares moving north and south from the base line is called a **range**. These are further broken down into 1-mile squares numbered 1 through 36 starting at the upper right corner of each township. These 1-mile squares are called **sections**. Each section can be further broken down into quarters which are labeled northeast, northwest, southeast, and southwest (fig. 6.16).

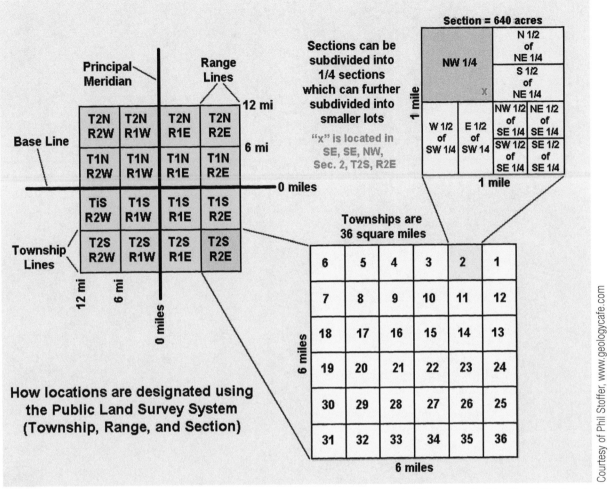

Figure 6.16   Grids created by the Public Land Survey. The largest units are 6 miles on each side. The "x" is located in the SE ¼, SE ¼, NW ¼, section 2, T2S, R2E.

Lab 7
Geologic Time

To accomplish the task of deciphering Earth's history, geologists have formulated several laws, principles, and doctrines that can be used to place geologic events in their proper sequence. Dating is done in two ways in geology. Absolute dating determines how many years ago an event occurred. The other method is relative dating in which one only knows the sequence of a set of events, but has no exact date for the events. Several attempts have been made to find a method of absolute dating. These attempts used the amount of salt in the ocean, the amount of sediment deposited on the sea floor, and Lord William Kelvin even attempted to determine the age of the Earth based on how long an iron ball took to cool.

After the discovery of radioactivity in 1896, it was soon realized that some elements existed in different forms and destructively decayed into other forms. These are called isotopes. Isotopes can be stable or unstable. The ones that decay, and are used in radioactive dating, are unstable isotopes. Isotopes vary in the number of neutrons in the nucleus of an atom but maintain the same number of protons. The process by which these elements change is called radioactive decay. The unstable isotope undergoing radioactive decay is called the parent isotope, and the resulting changed isotope is the daughter.

Absolute Dating

Igneous rocks are formed from the cooling of molten rock (magma) and igneous rocks are composed of various types of minerals which crystallize as the magma cools. These minerals are composed of atoms arranged in a repeating geometric structure, and different minerals have different chemical compositions (i.e., they are composed of different types of atoms). Initially, the magma or lava, being a fluid, is composed of different types of atoms moving around independently. As the magma cools (which occurs rapidly during an eruption and the magma is exposed to air and water), atoms begin to form bonds. The cooling process results in solid minerals, each with their own chemical compositions of elements.

The length of time elapsed since the element formed is based on the ratio of the parent isotope to the daughter isotope. The date is calculated based on the number of years required for ½ of the parent to decay to the daughter. This is called the half-life of the element. For example, carbon-14 decays

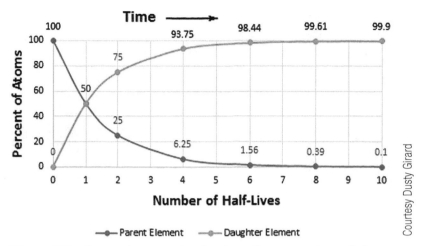

Figure 7.1   A generic curve showing how the parent element decays into the daughter

Table 7.1   The percentage of the parent and daughter element for each half-life

Number of Half-Lives	% of Parent Element	% of Daughter Element
0	100	0
1	50	50
2	25	75
3	12.5	87.5
4	6.25	93.75
5	3.13	96.88
6	1.56	98.44
7	0.78	99.22
8	0.39	99.61
9	0.2	99.8
10	0.1	99.9

to nitrogen-14 with a half-life of 5,730 years. If the original percentage of carbon-14 (the parent element) in the sample was 100% and original percentage of nitrogen-14 (the daughter element) was 0%, after 5,730 years there would be 50% of the parent and 50% of the daughter remaining. After another 5,730 years, there would be 25% of the parent and 75% of the daughter. After a third half-life, there would be 12.5% of the parent and 87.5% of the daughter element (fig. 7.1 and Table 7.1). For K^{40}, the half-life is about 1.25 billion years and the unstable K^{40} (potassium-40) decays into Ar^{40} (Argon-40). If we have a certain amount of K^{40}, and a certain amount of Ar^{40}, and we know that all the Ar^{40} started off as K^{40}, then we can calculate how long it has been since *all* of it was K^{40}.

Radiometric dating is not perfect. There is always a margin of error associated with these dates! For example, the half-life of Potassium-40 decaying to Argon-40 is 1.25 billion years. Typically, the margin of error is between 0.1% and 0.5% producing an error between 540,000 and 2.7 million years for a sample that is 540 million years old. Table 7.2 shows the half-life and dating ranges for some isotope pairs typically used in radiometric dating.

Table 7.2   Some common isotope pairs used for radiometric dating

Parent element	Half life	Daughter element	Dating range
Potassium-40	1.25 billion	Aragon-40	100,000 to 4.6 billion
Uranium-238	4.5 billion	Lead-206	10 million to 4.6 billion
Uranium-235	713 million	Lead-207	10 million to 4.6 billion
Thorium-232	14.1 billion	Lead-208	10 million to 4.6 billion
Rubidium-87	49 billion	Strontium-87	10 million to 4.6 billion
Carbon-14	5,730	Nitrogen-14	Up to 75,000

As an example, if a sample is tested and it is determined that is has 12.5% of the parent isotope and 87.5% of the daughter isotope, then using figure 7.1 and Table 7.1, we can determine 3 half-lives have passed for that sample. If the half-life for the isotope pair being used is 20 million years, then the sample is 60 million years old (3 half-lives * 20 million years each = 60 million years).

If a sample has passed through 2 half-lives, it would then contain 25% of the parent and 75% of the daughter isotope (See fig. 7.1 and Table 7.1). And, if the isotopes being tested were Carbon-14 and Nitrogen-14, the half-life is 5,730 years (See Table 7.2). Therefore, the sample would be 11, 460 years old (2 half-lives * 5,730 years each = 11,460 years).

Radiometric Dating with Different Rock Types

Radiometric dating works very well with igneous rocks because they often contain the isotope pairs needed for the process. However, sedimentary and metamorphic rocks are poor candidates for this dating method. Remember, sedimentary rocks are lithified from fragments of other rocks that have weathered. Therefore, any radiometric date of a sedimentary rock will indicate the age of the fragments the sedimentary rock is made of, not the age of the sedimentary rock that was created from those fragments. The weathering process also has the potential of removing some of the parent or daughter isotope thus causing errors in the analysis of the samples.

Metamorphic rocks are often heated to the point where some minerals in the original rock are melted and new minerals form in the metamorphic rock. This "resets the clock" of the ratio of parent to daughter isotopes in the sample. Therefore, any dating on these samples would be incorrect because it indicates the age of the last heating not the age of the metamorphic rock. If a sequence of sedimentary or metamorphic rocks is bounded by igneous rocks, the age of the igneous rocks can provide a relative date for the sedimentary or metamorphic rocks. By determining the age of the igneous rocks above and below the other rock types, an upper and lower age is determined and the sedimentary or metamorphic rocks must be within that age range.

Relative Dating

Obviously, when a geologist is doing field work it is impossible to carry the equipment necessary to perform absolute dating. In the field, a geologist uses a method called relative dating. This does not provide an exact date for an event or series of events, but does tell us the order in which the events occurred. To understand relative dating, we must first understand the only three scientific laws in geology. These laws were developed by Nicholas Steno and are known as Steno's Laws:

1. Law of Superposition – In a series of layered rocks, the rock layer on the bottom must be older than rock layer on the top, unless the rocks have been overturned. Think of a mason laying bricks, he cannot build a wall from the top down.

2. Law of Original Horizontality – Under normal circumstances, all layered rocks will be deposited in horizontal sheets parallel to the Earth's surface because of gravity.

3. Law of Lateral Continuity – Sediments deposited in a basin will form rock layers that are continuous from one side of the basin to the other.

Unconformities also play an important role in relative dating. An unconformity is a place in the rock record that represents non-deposition or erosion. In other words, the rock would have been exposed at the surface, so weathering could remove part of the layer or no deposition was occurring. Therefore, part of the rock record is missing. There are three types of unconformities: angular unconformities, disconformities, and nonconformities.

Angular unconformity

Older sediment layers have been tilted, truncated by erosion, and then a younger layer of sediments was deposited on the eroded surface. Figure 7.2 below is an example of an angular unconformity.

Disconformity

Parallel sediment deposition above and below the eroded surface (Figure 7.3). The layers above and below the disconformity will be comprised of sedimentary rock.

Nonconformity

Parallel sediment and igneous or metamorphic rocks (fig. 7.4). The layers above and below the nonconformity will consist of different rock types. Some situations where this may occur are when an eroded surface of sedimentary rock has been covered by a lava flow, or an exposed igneous or metamorphic layer has a deposition of sediment on top.

Courtesy Rick Lynn

Figure 7.2   Angular Unconformity. The layers of sedimentary rock at the bottom were deposited, tilted, eroded, and then the flat-lying layers at the top were deposited

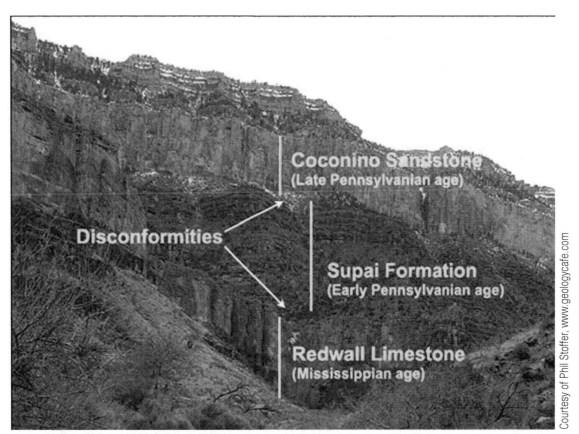

Figure 7.3   Disconformity. Parallel layers of sedimentary rocks with a break in the sedimentation

Figure 7.4   Nonconformity. Sedimentary rocks on the bottom ovelain by a lava flow

Another tool used in relative dating is the **principle of cross-cutting relationships.** If a series of layered rocks are cut by a fault or igneous intrusion, or the rocks are folded, the fault, intrusion, or fold must be younger than the layered rocks. In other words, the layers of rocks had to exist prior to being modified by the intrusion, fault, or folding. **The principle of inclusions** states that fragments of a rock included in another rock must be older than the layer of rock the fragments are included in. This occurs when a sequence of rocks is exposed at the surface and eroded. Fragments of the older rock layer will be lying on the surface and get incorporated into the next rock layer when deposition begins again. **Floral and Faunal Succession** states the observation that sedimentary rock strata contain fossilized flora and fauna, and that these fossils succeed each other vertically in a specific, reliable order that can be identified over wide horizontal distances. As one species dies

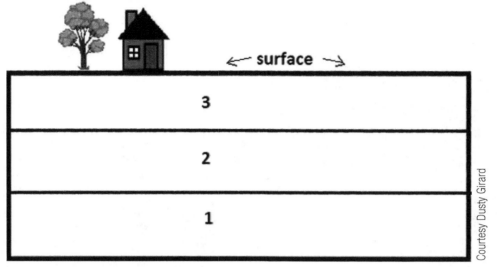

Figure 7.5 Simple ordering of layers

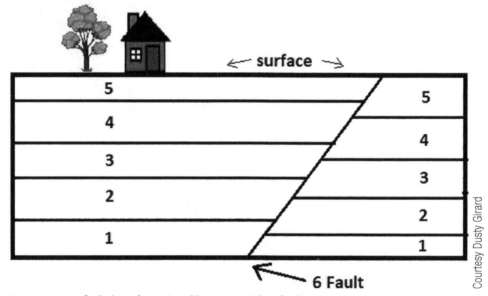

Figure 7.6 Ordering of events with cross-cutting fault

off, another emerges and the presence of specific fossils in a rock layer can be used to determine the approximate age.

In figure 7.5, we have a simple series of layered rocks. In this case, layer 1 must be older than layer 2, which is older than layer 3 with the surface being the youngest feature. From oldest to youngest we have layer 1, 2, 3, and then the surface.

Figure 7.6 is slightly more complex as a fault cross cuts the layered rocks. From oldest to youngest, the sequences of events are 1 through 5, then the fault (6), and finally the development of the surface.

In Figure 7.7, all of the lower sediment layers (C, B, A) are in order due to the Law of Superposition. The fault (E) occurred after the igneous intrusion (D) and the igneous intrusion is younger than C, B and A because of the principle of cross-cutting relationships. The unconformity (F) occurred after A

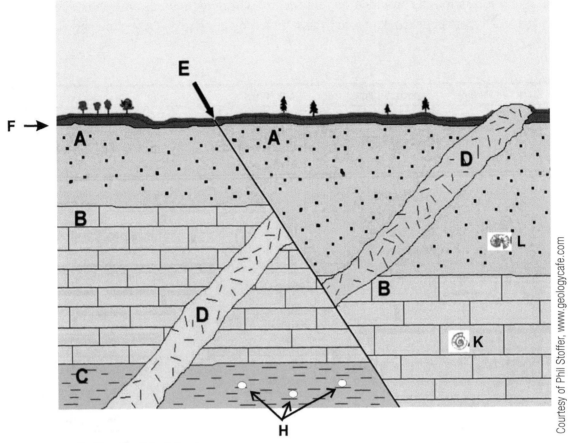

Courtesy of Phil Stoffer, www.geologycafe.com

Figure 7.7   Putting the Principles to use

but before D because the intrusion goes through to the surface. The principle of inclusions tells us the fragments H are older than sedimentary layer C. The principle of floral and faunal succession tells us fossil K is older than fossil L.

Fossils are the remains and traces of plants and animals that have lived on Earth in the past. While every fossil tells us something about the age of the rock it is found in, index fossils are the ones that tell us the most. Index fossils (also called key fossils or type fossils) are those that are used to define periods of geologic time.

A good index fossil is one with four characteristics: it is distinctive (easily identifiable), widespread, abundant, and limited in geologic time (short-lived). Because most fossil-bearing rocks formed in the ocean, the major index fossils are marine organisms, but certain land organisms are useful in young rocks found in specific regions.

Geologic Time Scale

The geologic time scale (GTS, fig. 7.8) is a system of chronological measurement that relates stratigraphy to time, and is used by geologists, paleontologists, and other earth scientists to describe the timing and relationships between events that have occurred throughout Earth's history. Based on radiometric dating techniques, the Earth is estimated to be about 4.6 billion years old. The geological time scale provides a means of mapping the history of the Earth. It combines estimates of the age of geological formations as provided by radiometric dating techniques with the direct evidence of sequences and events in the rock record as assembled by geologists (Absolute and Relative dating techniques).

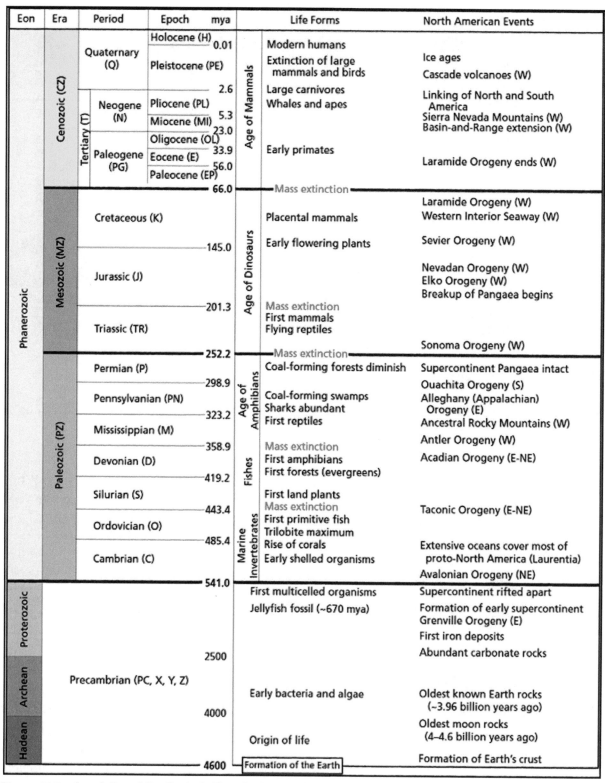

Eon	Era	Period	Epoch	mya	Life Forms	North American Events
Phanerozoic	Cenozoic (CZ)	Quaternary (Q)	Holocene (H)	0.01	**Age of Mammals** — Modern humans	Ice ages
			Pleistocene (PE)		Extinction of large mammals and birds	Cascade volcanoes (W)
		Neogene (N)	Pliocene (PL)	2.6	Large carnivores	Linking of North and South America
		Tertiary (T) — Neogene (N)	Miocene (MI)	5.3	Whales and apes	Sierra Nevada Mountains (W)
				23.0		Basin-and-Range extension (W)
		Paleogene (PG)	Oligocene (OL)			
			Eocene (E)	33.9	Early primates	
			Paleocene (EP)	56.0		Laramide Orogeny ends (W)
				66.0	— Mass extinction —	
	Mesozoic (MZ)	Cretaceous (K)			**Age of Dinosaurs** — Placental mammals	Laramide Orogeny (W)
						Western Interior Seaway (W)
				145.0	Early flowering plants	Sevier Orogeny (W)
		Jurassic (J)				Nevadan Orogeny (W)
						Elko Orogeny (W)
				201.3	Mass extinction	Breakup of Pangaea begins
		Triassic (TR)			First mammals Flying reptiles	
				252.2	— Mass extinction —	Sonoma Orogeny (W)
	Paleozoic (PZ)	Permian (P)			**Age of Amphibians** — Coal-forming forests diminish	Supercontinent Pangaea intact
				298.9		Ouachita Orogeny (S)
		Pennsylvanian (PN)			Coal-forming swamps Sharks abundant	Alleghany (Appalachian) Orogeny (E)
				323.2	First reptiles	Ancestral Rocky Mountains (W)
		Mississippian (M)				Antler Orogeny (W)
				358.9	Mass extinction	Acadian Orogeny (E-NE)
		Devonian (D)			**Fishes** — First amphibians First forests (evergreens)	
				419.2	First land plants	
		Silurian (S)			Mass extinction	Taconic Orogeny (E-NE)
				443.4	First primitive fish	
		Ordovician (O)			**Marine Invertebrates** — Trilobite maximum	
				485.4	Rise of corals	Extensive oceans cover most of proto-North America (Laurentia)
		Cambrian (C)			Early shelled organisms	Avalonian Orogeny (NE)
				541.0		
Proterozoic		Precambrian (PC, X, Y, Z)			First multicelled organisms	Supercontinent rifted apart
					Jellyfish fossil (~670 mya)	Formation of early supercontinent Grenville Orogeny (E)
						First iron deposits
				2500		Abundant carbonate rocks
Archean					Early bacteria and algae	Oldest known Earth rocks (~3.96 billion years ago)
				4000		Oldest moon rocks (4–4.6 billion years ago)
Hadean					Origin of life	Formation of Earth's crust
				4600	Formation of the Earth	

Figure 7.8   A variation of the Geologic Time Scale provided by the National Parks Service.

Geologic time scales can incorporate pivotal biologic and geologic events into eons, eras, periods, and epochs. We are currently in the Quaternary Period. Below is a copy of the Geologic Time Scale which includes major geologic and biologic events. Did you know the first dinosaurs were actually in the Triassic not Jurassic Period? Or that early humans were actually around over 1.6 million years ago?

Lab 8

Insolation, Seasons, and Climates

The relationship between Earth and the Sun is probably the most important astronomical phenomenon to life on this planet. The variations in solar energy striking the Earth as it rotates and revolves around the Sun cause the seasons. The amount of direct sunlight striking an area will have a great influence on the biomes. Weather is the state of the atmosphere at a particular place for a short period of time. The condition of the atmosphere at any location and time is described by measuring the four basic elements of weather: temperature, moisture, air pressure, and wind. Of all the controls that are responsible for causing variations in the weather elements, the amount of solar radiation received at any location is the most important. There are many factors attributed to the amount of solar radiation received, and one of the most significant is latitude.

Insolation

Insolation is a measure of solar radiation energy received on a given surface area and recorded during a given time. The amount of solar energy (radiation) striking the outer edge of the atmosphere is not uniform over the face of Earth at any one time. It is also not constant at any particular place throughout the year. Solar energy at any time and location is dependent on the Sun's intensity and duration. The angle at which the Sun's rays strike the surface of a location is called the intensity. Duration is the length of daylight at that particular location.

The langley is the standard unit of solar radiation and is equal to one calorie per square centimeter. The average intensity of solar radiation falling on a surface perpendicular to the beam at the outer edge of the atmosphere is referred to as the solar constant and is approximately 2 langleys per minute. As radiation passes through the atmosphere it undergoes reflection, absorption, and scattering. At any one location, less radiation reaches Earth's surface than was originally intercepted at the upper atmosphere.

Latitude and Solar Radiation

The amount of radiation striking a square meter at the outer edge of the atmosphere is not always the same on Earth's surface because it varies with latitude due to changing Sun angles. A Sun angle of 90 degrees (1 square meter) will create the same amount on the surface. However, if the Sun's angle is less than 90 degrees (lower toward the horizon), the solar radiation will be more spread out and cover a greater surface with less intensity (fig. 8.1).

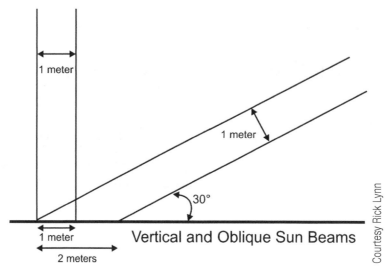

Figure 8.1   Notice the oblique beam is more spread out at the surface and covers a larger area

The amount of solar radiation received at a particular place does not remain constant throughout the year due to:

- Earth rotates on its axis and revolves around the Sun.

- The axis of Earth is inclined 23.5° from the perpendicular to the plane of its orbit.

- Throughout the year, the axis of Earth points to the same place in the sky, which causes the overhead (vertical – 90°) noon Sun to cross over the equator twice as it migrates from the Tropic of Cancer (23.5° N latitude) to the Tropic of Capricorn (23.5° S latitude) and back again to the Tropic of Cancer.

As a consequence, the position of the vertical or overhead noon Sun (subsolar point) shifts between the northern and southern hemispheres, causing variations in the intensity of solar radiation and changes in the length of daylight and darkness. This changing intensity and duration of solar energy and subsequent heating of the atmosphere result in the seasons experienced on Earth. To help understand how the intensity and duration of solar radiation varies throughout the year, the location of the direct Sunlight in relation to the Tropic of Cancer, Tropic of Capricorn, Arctic Circle, Antarctic Circle, and Equator is important. This progression of noon overhead Sunlight, referred to as the subsolar point, between 23.5° North and 23.5° South latitude is a result of the tilt of the axis (notice the tilt is 23.5° as well) and the Earth revolving around the Sun (fig. 8.2).

The Sun's rays are perpendicular (90°) to Earth's surface on the following dates and locations:

Date	Subsolar point location (90° noon sun)	Event (season begins)
March 21–22	0° (Equator)	Vernal Equinox (Spring)
June 21–22	23.5° N (Tropic of Cancer)	Summer Solstice (Summer)
September 22–23	0° (Equator)	Autumnal Equinox (Fall)
December 21–22	23.5°S (Tropic of Capricorn)	Winter Solstice (Winter)

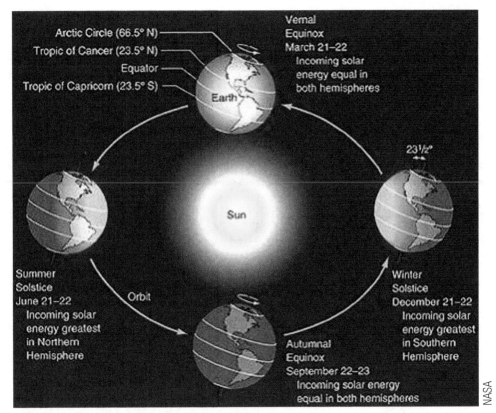

Figure 8.2 Seasons marked by Earth's angle tilted toward or away from the Sun

Notice the total migration of the subsolar point on the surface is from 23.5°N in the Summer to 23.5°S in the Winter, making the total migration 47° (23.5°N + 23.5°S = 47). Any date not on a seasonal change will have a different location between these two maximums of latitude for the subsolar point. An analemma is a tool used by navigators to know exactly what degree of latitude the subsolar point (90°) will fall on for any given day of the year (fig. 8.3).

The analemma can be used to determine the latitude of the noon 90° Sun or to calculate any given latitude based on the angle of the noon Sun at your location. For example, on October 31st, the subsolar point is located at 14°S latitude, so any location other than 14°S latitude will have a noon Sun angle of LESS than 90° (the Sun will not be directly overhead at noon). If you were located on the Equator on October 31st, the noon Sun would be located at 76° above the horizon (90° – 14° to get from the location of maximum Sunlight to the Equator = 76°). This is easier to visualize if you make a quick sketch of the globe with latitudes (fig. 8.4).

At Grayson College, we are located at approximately 34°N latitude, so on October 31st, how much Sunlight do we get at noon? Answer: On October 31st, the subsolar point is located at 14°S, so you need to go 14° to get to the equator then ANOTHER 34° to get to our location. Therefore, the total distance FROM the noon subsolar point is 48° (fig. 8.5). You subtract the difference from the original 90° to determine the angle of the Sun at noon at Grayson College on October 31st which is 42°. So, the Sun will be located at 42° above the horizon on that date at noon instead of directly overhead.

Another important factor to consider when looking at the amount of radiation hitting the Earth's surface, is the areas outside the total migration of the Sun during various times of the year. Only

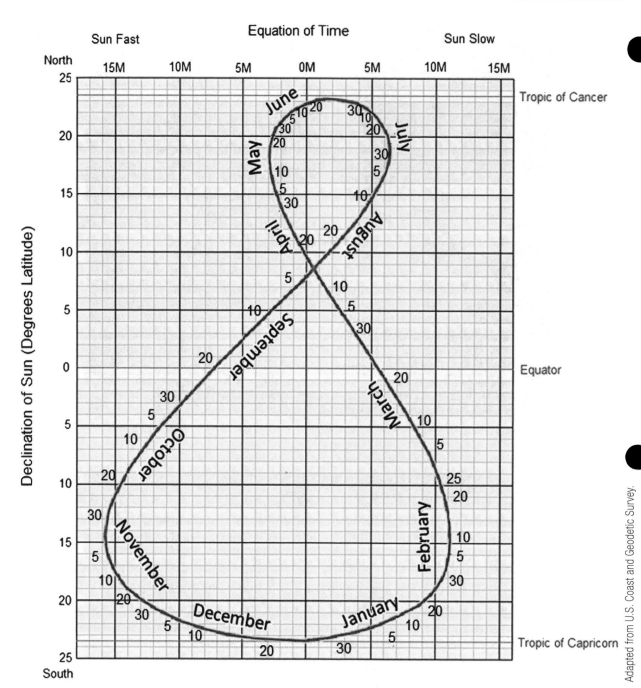

Figure 8.3   Analemma shows the date and location of the noon 90° Sun (subsolar point). Notice maximums at top and bottom correlate to the Summer and Winter Solstices and Equinoxes are at the Equator.

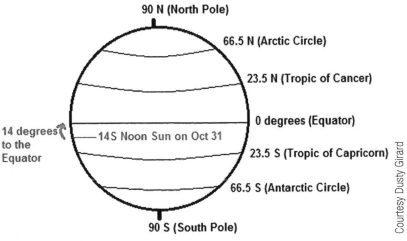

Figure 8.4   Standing on the Equator on October 31st, the noon Sun would be at 76° above the horizon

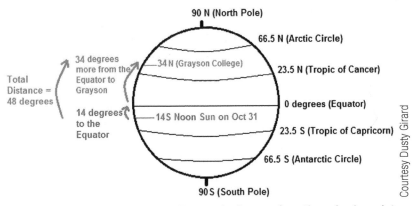

Figure 8.5   Calculate the total distance in degrees from the subsolar point then subtract from 90° to get angle of incidence at Grayson College on that date. (90°-48°=42°)

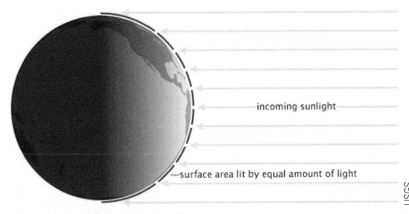

Figure 8.6   Circle of Illumination

half of Earth experiences Sunlight at a time which is referred to as the Circle of Illumination (fig. 8.6). This is why latitude plays an important role in solar changes.

This image depicts the Earth–Sun relationship and how only half of the Earth is affected at a time as it rotates on its axis. The furthest point out toward the Sun receives the most direct Sunlight. The angle of Sunlight for all other latitudes is less than 90° decreasing as you move from the spot closest to the Sun.

This relationship explains why the Arctic Circle and Antarctic Circle mark extremes and the margin at which the Sun's rays will not reach at specific times of the year. Notice in figure 8.2 during the Summer Solstice the Sun's rays do not go beyond 66.5°S (Antarctic Circle) making every point between there and the South Pole (90°S) in complete darkness. At the same time, the North Pole is always receiving low angles of solar radiation (constant light). During the Winter Solstice, the opposite occurs and the Arctic Circle (66.5°N) is without sunlight (constant darkness) while the South Pole is receiving continuous low angle radiation.

Location is relative to what season it is. So far, all the images and references have been made based on being located in the Northern Hemisphere. Consider if a person was located in Australia. Australia is located in the Southern Hemisphere. Considering the subsolar point hits the Tropic of Capricorn during December, what would be the Winter Solstice in the Northern Hemisphere actually marks the Summer Solstice in the Southern Hemisphere. Therefore, summer in Australia would be winter in North America and vice versa.

Latitude and Climate Zones

Air temperatures are not constant. They typically change based on the following factors:

- Through time at any one location

- With latitude because of the changing Sun angle and length of daylight

- With increasing altitude in lower atmosphere because the atmosphere is primarily heated from the bottom up

In general, daily temperatures that occur at any particular place are the result of long-wave (terrestrial) radiation being released at Earth's surface. Secondary factors such as cloud cover and cold air moving into the area can also cause variations. The primary reason for global variations in surface temperatures is the unequal distribution of solar radiation over the Earth. Among the most important secondary factors are differential heating of land and water, ocean currents, and differences in altitude. Continentality, or proximity to large bodies of water, creates less fluctuation in coastal zones. The interior of continents tend to be warmer due to being insulated from oceanic influences. Ocean currents carrying warm equatorial and cold polar waters also have an influence on coastal climates.

Examining global distributions of major atmospheric elements helps understand worldwide diversity. There are a variety of classification systems that simplify and describe the general weather conditions that occur at various places on Earth. The most widely used classification is the Köppen system which is based on the concept that climate is denoted by the native vegetation of an area. Classifications are based on combining average monthly and annual temperatures and precipitation for a particular area.

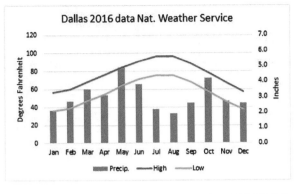

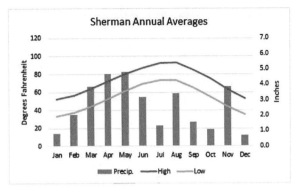

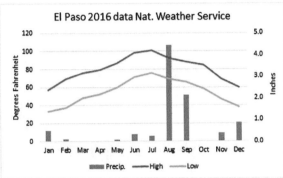

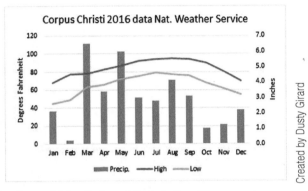

Figure 8.7   Compare several Texas locations and consider the variables that contribute to the differences in average temperature, and precipitation. Slight differences between Dallas and Sherman with greater differences between arid and coastal areas which would be reflected in the Köppen subtypes.

Whereas weather is a daily interpretation, climate is a summary of weather conditions at a particular place over a long period of time. Climatology involves studying the phenomena of weather characteristics of climates and climatic conditions. Climographs depict annual temperatures and precipitation by month (fig. 8.7). The annual range would be the difference between the highest and lowest variables throughout the course of the year for either temperature or precipitation. Climographs are typically used in the classification of climate zones.

Köppen Classification of Climates

The Köppen classification system was introduced in 1884, and has undergone several modifications since. However, it is still the best known and most used classification for presenting the general world patterns of climates. The Köppen climate classification scheme divides climates into five main groups, each having several types and subtypes. Each particular climate type is represented by a 2 to 4 letter symbol. The most recent modification to the system involves adding an additional group (H) for highlands classification to account for the significance of altitude on climate. Although not included with the principal climate groups, high-altitude (highlands) climates exist in all climate regions. They are the result of the changes in radiation, temperature, humidity, precipitation, and atmospheric pressure that take place with elevation and the orientation of mountain slopes. Descriptions of Köppen groups are detailed and based on specific temperature and precipitation qualifiers. We will focus on the main groups.

Class A: Tropical Moist, Megathermal

Temperature of the coldest month is > 18°C and annual precipitation > 59". Typically located 15° to 25° north and south of the equator, respectively. This is the climate where the most water- and heat-demanding crops (e.g. for instance oil palm and rubber) are grown. The climate is also ideal for yams, cassava, maize, rice, bananas, and sugarcane.

Class B: Dry; Arid/Semi-Arid

Arid climates are where annual evaporation and transpiration exceed annual precipitation. They are typically located in large continental regions of mid-latitudes and 20°–35° north and south of the equator. Even the wettest variants of this climate are characterized by a marked dry season. The climate is mostly unsuitable for crops that require year-round moisture. The main crops are usually millet, sorghum, and groundnuts. Sunshine is usually high, which leads to high productivity where a sufficiently long rainy season or irrigation ensures a sufficient water supply. Rice, sugarcane, and maize are also common crops under this climate. The two main subclasses refer to the dominant vegetation types: **BS** (steppe climate) and **BW** (desert).

Class C: Temperate; Moist mid-latitude with mild winters, Mesothermal

Average temperature of the coldest month is between −3°C and 18°C, and average temperature of the warmest month is >10°C resulting in mild winters with warm and humid summers. Summer months are dominated by convective thunderstorms and the winter by the mid-latitude cyclone. Typically located 30° to 50° north and south of the equator, the main crops are the temperate cereals such as wheat, barley, and Irish (white) potatoes. An important variant of this climate is the Mediterranean climate (**Cs**), characterized by the olive tree, and also very suitable for grapes.

Class D: Cold; Moist mid-latitude with severe winters, Microthermal

Average temperature of the warmest month is >10°C, and the coldest month is < -30°C. Microthermal climates are located poleward after the 'C' regions having much harsher winters with severe snowstorms, strong winds, and cold air masses. This climate grows essentially the same crops as the temperate climate, but seasons tend to be shorter and limited at the beginning and end by frost.

Class E: Polar

Average temperature of the warmest month is <10°C. No crops are grown under this climate. The two main subdivisions - **ET** (tundra, average temperature of warmest month > 0°C) and **EF** (no month with temperature > 10°C) are sometimes qualified by **d** if the average temperature of coldest month < -38°C.

Class H: Highlands

These are climates that are strongly influenced by the effects of altitude. Rapid climate changes occur over short distances due to the rapid elevation changes in mountainous terrain. As a result, the climate of such locations is rather different from places with low elevations at similar latitudes.

Each major group is divided into smaller groups based on precipitation and temperature with the second letter based on precipitation patterns and the third on temperature patterns (fig. 8.8).

In order to be specific when describing a climate region, it is important to designate the sub-divisions order to have a comprehensive understanding of the region. Consider the Köppen group 'B', arid, which can be found on almost every inhabited continent. But, arid regions vary greatly. For example, El Paso, Texas, and the Sahara Desert are considered arid, 'B' climates. They can be further classified by the third sub-division. El Paso is considered BWk and the Sahara Desert is BWh. This also is reflected in the difference in vegetation found in both regions. The chart (fig. 8.9) gives a description of some of the different climate groups with subdivisions from the National Oceanic and Atmospheric Administration (NOAA).

Second letter divisions:	Third letter divisions:
f - wet year-round	a - hot summers
s - dry summer season	b - warm summers
w - dry winter season	c - cool summers
m - monsoon	d - very cold winters
S - Steppe, semi-arid	h - dry and hot
W - Desert, arid and semi-arid	k - dry and cold
T - tundra	
F - ice cap	

Figure 8.8 Description of subdivisions for Köppen Classifications

A	**Equitorial Climates**	**Minimum temperature ≥ +18°C**
Af	Equatorial rainforest	No dry season. The driest month has at least 2.36" (60 mm) of rain. Rainfall is generally evenly distributed throughout the year. All average monthly temperatures are greater than 64°F (18°C).
Am	Equatorial monsoon	Pronounced wet season. Short dry season. There are one or more months with less than 2.36" (60 mm). All average monthly temperatures are greater than 64°F (18°C). Highest annual temperature occurs just prior to the rainy season.
Aw	Equatorial savanna	Winter dry season. There are more than two months with less than 2.36" (60 mm) in winter. All average monthly temperatures are greater than 64°F (18°C).
B	**Arid Climates**	**Annual evaporation > precipitation**
BS	Mid-latitude desert	Mid-latitude desert. Evaporation exceeds precipitation on average but is less than half potential evaporation. Average temperature is less than 64°F (18°C). Winter has below freezing temperatures.
BW	Subtropical desert	Low-latitude desert. Evaporation exceeds precipitation on average but is less than half potential evaporation. Average temperature is more than 64°F (18°C). Frost is absent or infrequent.
C	**Warm Temperate**	**Minimum temperature between - 3°C and +18°C**
Cfa	Humid subtropical	Mild with no dry season, hot summer. Average temperature of warmest months are over 72°F (22°C). Average temperature of coldest month is under 64°F (18°C). Year around rainfall but highly variable.
Cfb	Marine west coast	Mild with no dry season, warm summer. Average temperature of all months is lower than 72°F (22°C). At least four months with average temperatures over 50°F (10°C). Year around equally spread rainfall.
Csa	Mediterranean	Mild with dry, hot summer. Warmest month has average temperature more than 72°F (22°C). At least four months with average temperatures over 50°F (10°C). Frost danger in winter. At least three times as much precipitation during wettest winter months as in the driest summer month.
Cwa	Humid subtropical	Mild with dry winter, hot summer
D	**Snow Climates**	**Minimum temperature ≤ - 3°C**
Df	Humid continental	Snow climate, fully humid
Dfb	Humid continental	Humid with severe winter, no dry season, warm summer
Dw	Humid continental	Snow climate with dry winter
E	**Polar Climates**	**Maximum temperature < +10°C**
ET	Tundra	Polar tundra, no true summer; maximum temperature between 0°C and + 10°C
EF	Ice Cap	Perennial ice; maximum temperature < 0°C
H	Highlands	Complex Zones: Can encompass any of the above classifications due to the mountainous terrain.

NOAA

Figure 8.9   Chart of selected Köppen groups and sub-divisions. This is not a complete list of all climates.

Using what you learned

On the maps below, notice the similarities between global temperatures (fig. 8.10) and the Köppen Classifications (fig. 8.11). Remember the influence solar radiation has on surface temperatures and compare what you have learned about the Sun's migration over the surface to the map depicting average annual land temperatures around the world. Regions that receive the most Sunlight tend to be warmer and it gets progressively get cooler moving away from the Equator. Also notice the lower temperature regions over the coastal areas away from large land masses (continentality).

Tropical regions tend to be centered on the Equator; desert/arid locations are associated with latitudes 30° North and South with the temperate zones and the polar regions around 60° North and South. Native vegetation is influenced by annual temperature and precipitation therefore different crops would be better suited at different latitudes.

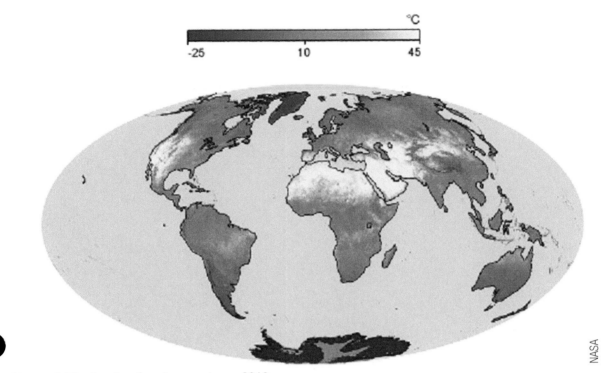

Figure 8.10 Land surface temperatures, 2016

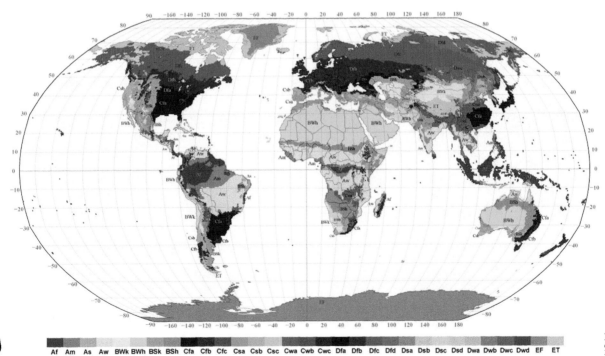

Figure 8.11 Distribution of Köppen classifications

Lab 9

Atmospheric Conditions

Atmospheric Heating

Atmospheric heating is caused by the following three things:

1. the ability of atmospheric gases to absorb radiation

2. the amount of solar radiation reaching the surface

3. nature of the surface material

The quantity of radiation that reaches the surface and how the Earth re-radiates that radiation determine the extent of atmospheric heating. The atmosphere selectively allows radiation from the Sun to reach the Earth. Short wavelength (ultraviolet) radiation passes through the atmosphere but when it is absorbed and radiated back off of the surface, it becomes long wavelength (Infrared) radiation (fig. 9.1). As this radiation (terrestrial radiation) is absorbed by gases in the atmosphere, it causes atmospheric heating.

Different materials on Earth's surface absorb and re-radiate heat in different ways. Some materials reflect radiation. This is called albedo which is the reflectivity of a substance. Surfaces with high albedo reflect the shortwave and do not absorb and convert the radiation into long wave radiation.

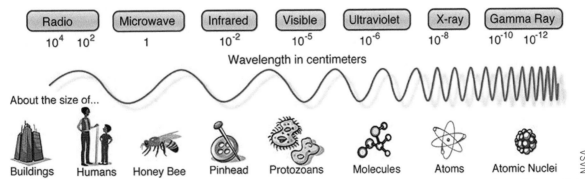

Figure 9.1 The spectrum of radiation. The human eye can only detected a very small portion of the radiation spectrum. Earth is heated as long wavelength radiation is converted to short wavelength radiation which is trapped by the atmosphere

Therefore, surfaces with high albedos contribute less to atmospheric heating. White surfaces tend to reflect more radiation (high albedo) whereas dark surfaces (low albedo) tend to absorb more radiation. White surfaces reflect short wave radiation therefore, atmospheric heating is reduced. Cloud cover decreases surface heating by reflecting sunlight back into space. Clouds also reduce the amount of heat loss to space which increases atmospheric heating (the greenhouse effect). Snow and glaciers also increase the albedo effect while fresh plowed ground or deforested regions lower the albedo effect and heat increases (fig. 9.2 and 9.3).

Simplified versions (don't laugh at the car!):

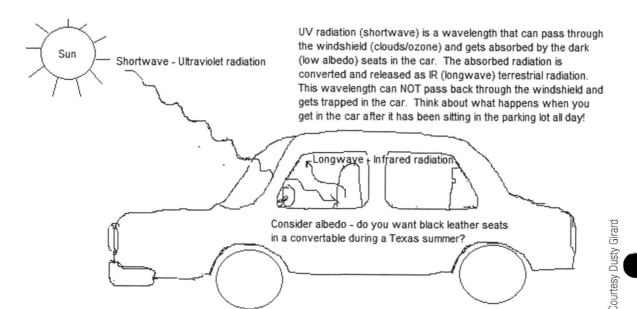

UV radiation (shortwave) is a wavelength that can pass through the windshield (clouds/ozone) and gets absorbed by the dark (low albedo) seats in the car. The absorbed radiation is converted and released as IR (longwave) terrestrial radiation. This wavelength can NOT pass back through the windshield and gets trapped in the car. Think about what happens when you get in the car after it has been sitting in the parking lot all day!

Consider albedo - do you want black leather seats in a convertable during a Texas summer?

Courtesy Dusty Girard

Figure 9.2   Short wavelength or ultraviolet radiation can pass through the windows in your car but when reflected off of the interior the radiation is converted to long wavelength (infrared radiation) which is trapped in the car causing the temperature to rise

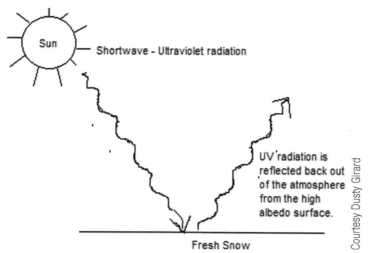

UV radiation is reflected back out of the atmosphere from the high albedo surface.

Fresh Snow

Courtesy Dusty Girard

Figure 9.3   Ultraviolet radiation passes through the Earth's atmosphere but is reflected from the surface as infrared radiation which is trapped by gases in the atmosphere which warms the planet

Vapor Pressure, Humidity, and Dew Point

As gas molecules move around and collide with objects (including other molecules), pressure is exerted. The atmosphere is a collection of gas molecules which are in constant motion. The pressure exerted by water molecules is called vapor pressure and is expressed in millibars. Water vapor makes up about 4% of the total atmosphere. The pressure exerted by all of the gases in the atmosphere is about 1,000 millibars. When the atmosphere is saturated, pressure exerted by water vapor molecules is called the saturation vapor pressure. The ratio of the actual vapor pressure exerted by molecules of water vapor versus the saturation vapor pressure at the same temperature is called the saturation ratio. Relative humidity is this ratio multiplied by 100 therefore:

Relative Humidity=(Vapor Pressure/Saturation Vapor Pressure)*100

In this case, if the vapor pressure is 42 and the saturation vapor pressure is 65, the formula becomes:

Relative Humidity=(42/65)*100

Relative Humidity=64.62%

The relative humidity describes how far from saturation the atmosphere is. Saturated air has a relative humidity of 100%. Temperature affects relative humidity. Warmer air has a higher saturation mixing ratio than cooler air at a constant atmospheric pressure. As temperature increases, the vapor per kilogram of dry air increases as well. The dew point is the temperature to which air must be cooled to reach saturation without changing the pressure. When the dew point is reached, the relative humidity is 100% and dew forms as moisture condenses out of the atmosphere.

Equivalent Temperatures

Wind cools the body by evaporating perspiration from the skin surface, thus carrying heat away. As wind speed increases, the amount of wind chill increases. The wind chill describes the increased loss of heat by the movement of air. The original formula was based on wind speed 10 m above the ground and translates a person's heat loss under current temperature, and wind conditions into a temperature that would be required to produce the same heat loss with a 3 knot wind. In 2001, the National Weather Service revised the formula to use wind speed 1.5 m above the ground and takes into account the ability of the wind to remove heat from a person's face. The revised formula is:

Wind chill temperature = 35.74 + 0.6215T - 35.75(V ^0.16) + 0.4275T(V^0.16)

In the formula, V is in the wind speed in statute miles per hour, and T is the temperature in degrees Fahrenheit. The "^" symbol means 'raise to the power of.' Remember, the calculated value for wind chill will be below the actual air temperature. For example, if the air temperature is 30°F and the wind speed is 10 miles per hour (MPH), the formula becomes:

Wind Chill Temperature = 35.74 + 0.6215(30)–35.75(10^.16)+.4275(30)(10^.16)

Wind Chill Temperature = 35.74+18.645-35.75(1.45)+.4275(30)(1.45)

Wind Chill Temperature = 35.74+18.645-51.67+18.53

Wind Chill Temperature = 21.25 (when the actual temperature is 30°F, wind 10mph)

The heat index is a calculated value based on the actual air temperature and the relative humidity. If the temperature is high but the humidity is low, the heat index will be below the actual air temperature because perspiration from the body evaporates quicker keeping the body cool. If the temperature and humidity are both high, the heat index will exceed the actual temperature because perspiration cannot evaporate and cool the body.

Pressure

The force exerted by the weight of the atmosphere is called atmospheric pressure. This varies, primarily because of changes in temperature as warm air is less dense than cold air. A tall column of warm air will apply the same pressure as a short column of cool air. Atmospheric pressure is measured using a barometer. Two units of measurement are commonly used, inches of mercury and millibars. Inches of mercury literally refers to the height a column of mercury will rise to in a glass tube that has been inverted in a reservoir of mercury (fig. 9.4). The millibar is a measurement of the actual force pressing down on a surface. Standard pressure at sea level is 29.92 inches of mercury or 1,013.2 millibars. A pressure below the standard is called low pressure whereas pressure above the standard is called high pressure. To convert from millibars to inches of mercury multiply by .02953. So (1,013.2*.02953)=29.92. To convert from inches of mercury to millibars, divide inches of mercury by .02953, therefore (29.92/.02953)=1,013.2

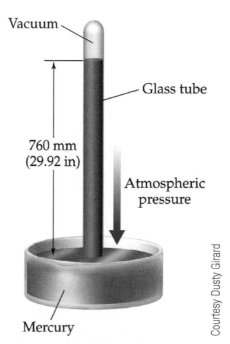

Figure 9.4   Diagram of a mercury barometer. Atmospheric pressure pushes down on the mercury in the glass bowl and forces the mercury up the tube. The height the mercury raises in the tube is measured to determine barometric pressure.

Urban Heat Island Effect

As urban areas develop, changes occur in their landscape. Buildings, roads, and other infrastructure replace open land and vegetation. Surfaces that were once permeable and moist become impermeable and dry. These changes cause urban regions to become warmer than their rural surroundings, forming an "island" of higher temperatures in the landscape (fig. 9.5).

Heat islands occur on the surface and in the atmosphere. On a hot, sunny summer day, the Sun can heat dry, exposed urban surfaces, such as roofs and pavement, to temperatures 50–90°F (27–50°C) hotter than the air, while shaded or moist surfaces—often in more rural surroundings—remain close to air temperatures. Surface urban heat islands are typically present day and night, but tend to be strongest during the day when the Sun is shining.

In contrast, atmospheric urban heat islands are often weak during the late morning and throughout the day and become more pronounced after sunset due to the slow release of heat from urban infrastructure. The annual mean air temperature of a city with 1 million people or more can be 1.8–5.4°F (1–3°C) warmer than its surroundings. On a clear, calm night, however, the temperature difference can be as much as 22°F (12°C).

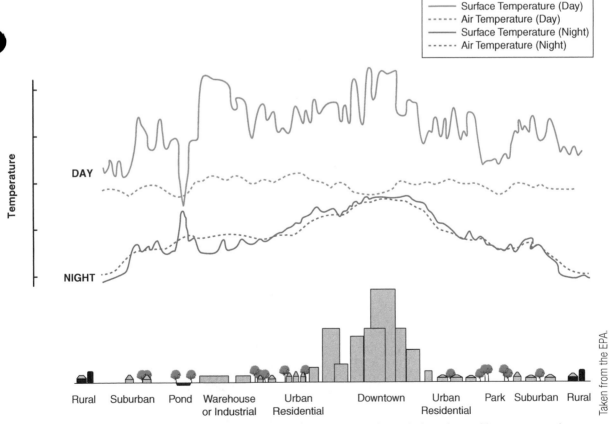

Figure 9.5   Urban Heat Island Effect: Notice the higher temperatures with proximity to large cities versus rural areas.

Air Masses, Fronts, Clouds, and Weather Maps

Types of Air Masses

An **air mass** is a large body of air whose temperature and moisture content are similar in any horizontal direction. These can cover thousands of square kilometers and form when air stagnates in one location for a long period of time. The air mass reflects the conditions of the surface over which it formed and can be hot or cold and moist or dry.

- Polar (P) air masses form at a latitude of 60° or higher and are cold.

- Tropical (T) air masses form within 30° of the equator and are warm.

- Arctic (A) air masses form over the Arctic and are very cold.

- Continental (c) air masses form over large land masses and are dry.

- Maritime (m) air masses form over the ocean and are moist.

The letter classifications for these air masses can be combined to indicate in greater detail the characteristics of the air mass. For example, a tropical air mass may form over the sea or land. If the tropical air mass formed over the sea, it would be warm and wet with a two letter classification of mT. If the tropical air mass formed over the land, it would be warm and dry and would have a two letter classification of cT.

Air mass modification occurs as an air mass moves from one location to another. The air mass exchanges heat and moisture with the underlying surface. Heat exchanges between the air mass and the surface have the greatest effect on lower portions of the air mass. The rate of moisture exchange is greatest when the relative humidity is low and the surface is wet. As continental polar (cP) air masses move over bodies of warm water such as the Great Lakes and the North Atlantic, the air saturates quickly forming a **steam fog**. These fog banks can be 1,500 m thick and contain swirling columns of fog called **steam devils**. In some cases, cP air masses moving over the Great Lakes increase snowfall downwind. These are referred to as **lake-effect snows**. During the winter, cP air masses may stall over the Gulf of Mexico. These air masses are modified by the warm waters of the Gulf over several days and are drawn back to the north. These air masses may be reclassified as mT (maritime Tropical) because of the increase in moisture and warmth of the air mass. These are called **return flow events.**

Weather Fronts

As different air masses come in contact, they slowly mix together over a period of several days. The transition zone between two different air masses is called a **front**. Fronts can be hundreds of kilometers long and exist as long as the identity of the two air masses remains distinct and separate. Fronts are classified by the temperature changes that occur as they pass a given point. If the temperature will drop with the front's passage, it is a **cold front**; if the temperature increases with the passage of the front, it is a **warm front**. Cold fronts have very steep boundaries at their leading edge (fig. 10.1). This causes warm air at the leading edge of the front to rise rapidly. This leads to the development of intense thunderstorms. However, these storms are isolated to the frontal boundary and tend to move quickly over a given location. Cold fronts vary in speed from almost stationary up to 50 km/hr. The triangles on the map symbol (fig. 10.1) indicate the direction of movement of the cold front. Cold fronts are associated with regions of low pressure relative to the region in front of and behind the front. The leading edge of a cold front is steepest at the surface and tends to rise about 1 km for every 50–100 km of horizontal distance along the surface.

After the passing of a warm front, the air is warmer and typically more humid. The temperature will rise slowly as the front approaches, and then increase rapidly with the passage of the warm front. As with a cold front, warm fronts are associated with areas of low pressure; however, the pressure change with a warm front is not as dramatic as the pressure changes with a cold front. The vertical slope of the warm front is shallower than a cold front. Typically, a warm front rises about 1 km for every 200 km of horizontal distance. Air in warm fronts glides up gradually over the cooler air mass it is replacing. This process is called **overrunning**. As the warm front rides over the colder air, steady, moderate rain will persist over large areas. If the cold air mass being replaced is below

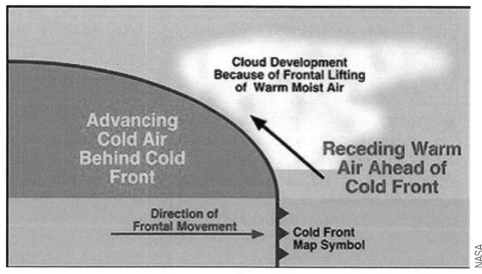

Figure 10.1   Advancing cold fronts generate thunderstorms as warm air rapidly moves vertically over the cold air

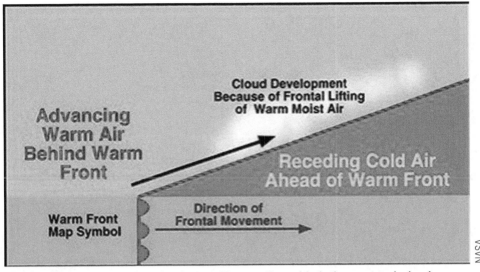

Figure 10.2   Advancing warm fronts ride over the cold air they are replacing because the warm air is less dense than the cold air

Figure 10.3   Map symbol for a stationary front

freezing, rain falling out of the warm air may freeze producing sleet or freezing rain. The half-circles on the map symbol indicate the direction of the frontal movement (fig. 10.2).

Stationary fronts are the result of two air masses colliding with no movement occurring on the surface. In spite of the lack of surface movement, overrunning can occur at higher elevations causing weather conditions to be similar to a warm front. This can create long periods of light precipitation on the cold side of the stationary front. High winds may exist at upper elevations as the two air masses struggle to merge. The map symbol for a stationary front is shown in figure 10.3.

An **occluded front** is when a fast-moving cold front catches up with a warm front. This creates a frontal line between two polar air masses with the warm air mass lifted above them (fig. 10.4). The weather preceding the occluded front will be much like the weather preceding a warm front with light, steady rain. After the front passes, the weather will be similar to a cold front with intense storms along a narrow line.

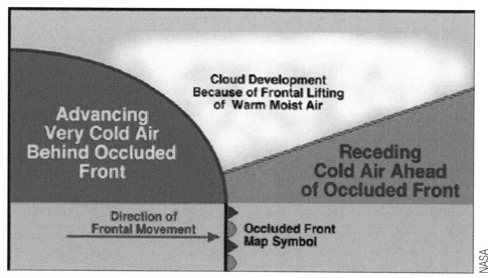

Figure 10.4   The occluded front is a meeting of two cold air masses with the warm air mass lofted above them

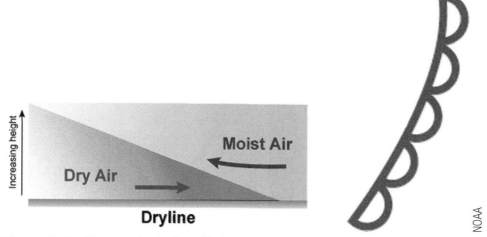

Figure 10.5   Diagram of a dryline with the map symbol

A **dryline** is a zone defined by moisture and wind rather than temperature. These are common in the late spring as dry cT air is drawn north from Mexico into Texas and Oklahoma. About 15 km east of the dryline, air converges and raises creating storms much like a cold front. The temperature difference along a dryline can be small, but the dew point can be huge as warm moist mT air is brought north from the Gulf of Mexico across east Texas (fig. 10.5).

High pressure systems are represented on a weather map by a capital H. High pressure is any area where the atmospheric pressure is above normal sea level pressure of 1,013.2 millibars. Wind around high pressure systems rotates clockwise. Low pressure systems are represented on a weather map by a capital L. Low pressure is any area where the atmospheric pressure is below normal sea level pressure of 1,013.2 millibars. Wind around low pressure systems rotates counter-clockwise. Tornadoes are high speed winds centered around very narrow regions of low pressure. Hurricanes are areas of intense low pressure.

Clouds
Cirro-form

Cirro-form clouds (fig. 10.6) form at high altitudes (6km or more) and are typically composed of ice crystals. These clouds are typically thin and white, but the setting Sun can produce an array of colors as light travels through these clouds. These clouds typically form in fair weather and point in the direction of air flow at their elevation. There are three types of cirro-form clouds: cirrus, cirrostratus, and cirrocumulus. Cirrus clouds are wispy and feathery and often indicate and approaching warm front. Cirrus clouds may thicken into other types of clouds with an approaching warm front. Cirrostratus clouds form a widespread, veil-like layer in the atmosphere. As Sun or Moon light refracts through the ice crystals, a "halo" often forms around these clouds. Cirrocumulus clouds are layered clouds that may have a lumpy appearance and may line up in rows indicating areas of ascending air (cloudy) and descending air (clear areas).

NOAA

Figure 10.6 An example of cirro-form clouds. These are typically thin and white and form at high altitudes

Nimbostratus

Nimbostratus clouds (fig. 10.7) form between 2.1 and 4.6 km. The term nimbus comes from a Latin term meaning "rain." These clouds bring steady precipitation and lower toward the ground as rain begins to fall. Other clouds that form at these mid-level altitudes include altostratus and altocumulus. Altostratus clouds typically do not produce precipitation and usually have a flat, uniform texture. Altocumulus clouds are heap-like clouds that show some elements of convection (heat movement). Like cirrocumulus clouds, altocumulus clouds may line themselves up in rows indicating areas of ascending and descending air. If these clouds have some elevation extent, it may indicate an area of instability, especially in the morning hours.

Figure 10.7 Nimbostratus clouds form at mid-levels in the atmosphere and often bring precipitation

Cumulo-form

Cumulo-form clouds (fig. 10.8) look like large, fluffy stacks of cotton balls and show the thermal uplift of air in the atmosphere. Their flat base indicates the level at which condensation is taking place and the elevation to which they rise is dependent on the humidity of the rising air column. These clouds have a lower base with more humid air and can reach over 18 km.

Figure 10.8 Cumulo-form clouds have a fluffy, cotton ball appearance

Strato-form

Strato-form clouds (fig. 10.9) have a rather featureless lower layer and often cover the entire sky like a blanket (stratus is Latin for blanket) making for gray and dull weather. The bases are usually only a few hundred meters above the ground and often reach the ground surface, producing fog over hilly or mountainous areas.

Figure 10.9   Strato-form clouds make for a dull, gray looking day

Wall clouds

Wall clouds (fig. 10.10) result when a rain-free area of the cloud lowers locally during a strong thunderstorm. This indicates a strong updraft where rising air causes a low pressure area below the main updraft area in the cloud. This will increase condensation and cloud formation under the primary cloud base. The clouds form in many shapes and sizes and may exhibit strong upward motion or rotation. The rotation may lead to the development of a tornado.

Figure 10.10 Wall clouds may indicate the formation of a tornado

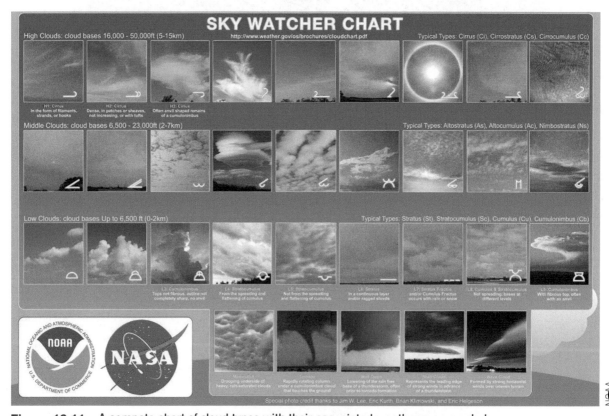

Figure 10.11 A compete chart of cloud types with their associated weather map symbols.

Weather Maps

In order to understand, analyze, and predict weather, observers at hundreds of weather stations throughout the United States collect and record weather data several times a day. This information is forwarded to the National Weather Service where a computer processes the data along with satellite data and maps the results. Weather maps are then distributed to any interested individual or agency. Weather forecasts, such as this one, provide critical information to many people, including farmers, construction workers, and those planning a trip to the beach. In severe weather situations, short-term forecasts, watches, and warnings can help save lives and protect property.

Weather Station Data

Meteorologists have developed a system for coding weather data to manage the information and create accurate maps. The key to understanding a weather map is to understand the weather symbols that are used on the map (fig. 10.12). Below are some keys of symbols used in surface station models.

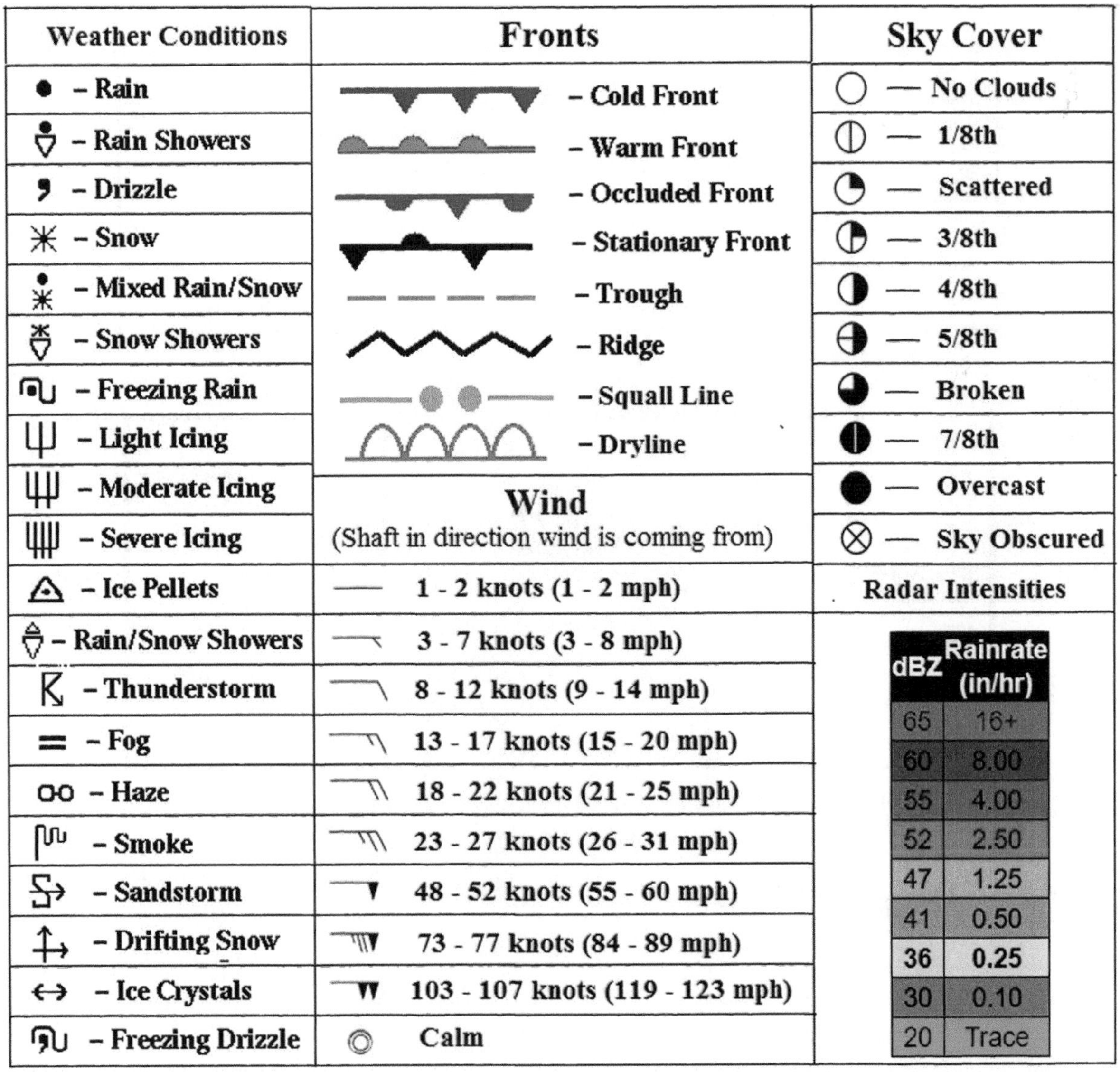

Weather Conditions	Fronts	Sky Cover
● – Rain	– Cold Front	○ — No Clouds
▽ – Rain Showers	– Warm Front	◑ — 1/8th
⁹ – Drizzle	– Occluded Front	◔ — Scattered
✳ – Snow	– Stationary Front	◓ — 3/8th
✳ – Mixed Rain/Snow	– Trough	◑ — 4/8th
♉ – Snow Showers	– Ridge	◕ — 5/8th
⌀ᴜ – Freezing Rain	– Squall Line	◕ — Broken
Ⴠ – Light Icing	– Dryline	◕ — 7/8th
ⴡ – Moderate Icing	**Wind**	● — Overcast
ⴢ – Severe Icing	(Shaft in direction wind is coming from)	⊗ — Sky Obscured
△ – Ice Pellets	— 1 - 2 knots (1 - 2 mph)	**Radar Intensities**
♉ – Rain/Snow Showers	— 3 - 7 knots (3 - 8 mph)	
R – Thunderstorm	— 8 - 12 knots (9 - 14 mph)	
= – Fog	— 13 - 17 knots (15 - 20 mph)	
ꝏ – Haze	— 18 - 22 knots (21 - 25 mph)	
⌐ᴜᴜ – Smoke	— 23 - 27 knots (26 – 31 mph)	
⇛ – Sandstorm	— 48 - 52 knots (55 - 60 mph)	
⇑ – Drifting Snow	— 73 - 77 knots (84 - 89 mph)	
↔ – Ice Crystals	— 103 - 107 knots (119 - 123 mph)	
⌀ᴜ – Freezing Drizzle	◎ Calm	

Radar Intensities table:

dBZ	Rainrate (in/hr)
65	16+
60	8.00
55	4.00
52	2.50
47	1.25
41	0.50
36	0.25
30	0.10
20	Trace

Courtesy Dusty Girard

Figure 10.12   Standardized symbols used for weather charts

Surface station models incorporate these symbols onto surface maps. When plotting barometric pressure in millibars for a weather station, to conserve space, the initial number 9 or 10 is omitted and the last digit is tenths of a millibar. For example, on a map a barometric pressure of 045 would be 1004.5 or 211 would be 1021.1.

Weather symbols are used to plot current conditions on a map to quickly convey information about conditions at different locations. A simple version of weather symbol is shown in Figure 10.13, but they can be more complex when all aspects are plotted by the weather station. For example, visibility in miles will appear in front of the weather symbol, a symbol expressing change in pressure in the last 3 hours will be below the pressure amount (indicating if pressure has increased or decreased and by how much in tenths of millibars), and cloud types with high-level clouds then mid-level clouds located above the weather symbol and low-level clouds with the height of the base of that cloud in hundreds of feet is located below the weather symbol (fig. 10.14).

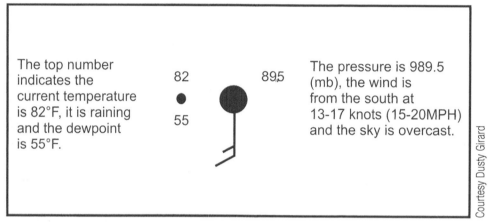

Figure 10.13   A simplified weather map symbol

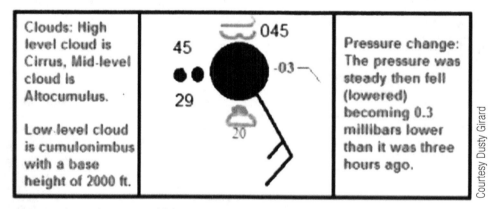

Figure 10.14   A more complete version of a weather map symbol indicating the change in pressure and type and height of cloud cover

Analyzing Weather Maps

Once you can read a station plot you can begin to perform map analyses. Meteorologists use the station plots to draw lines of constant pressure (isobars, fig. 10.15), temperature (isotherms, fig. 10.16), and dewpoint (isodrosotherms, fig. 10.17) to achieve an understanding of the current state of the atmosphere. This knowledge ultimately leads to better weather forecasts, watches, and warnings.

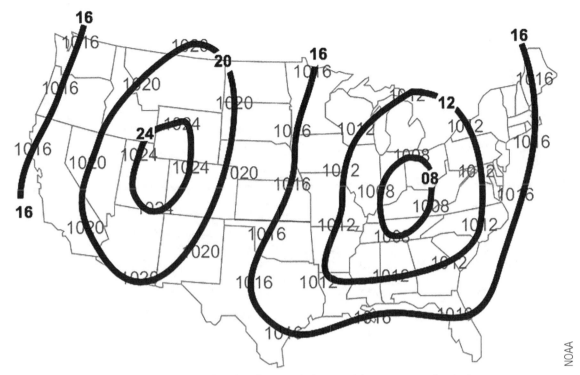

Figure 10.15 A sample map showing the changes in barometric pressure using isobars

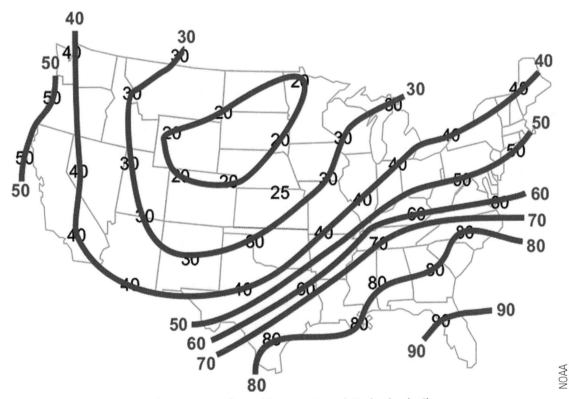

Figure 10.16 This map shows areas of equal temperature plotted using isotherms

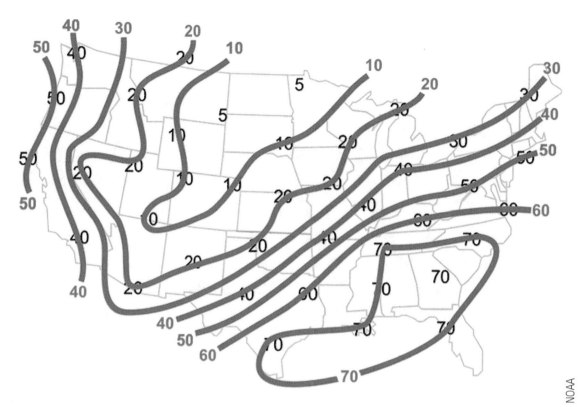

Figure 10.17   This sample map shows areas of equal dew point temperature plotted using isodrosotherms.

Watches Versus Warnings

A watch is issued when the weather conditions are favorable for a certain type of weather to occur. A warning is issued when a certain type of weather is happening now. Therefore, a thunderstorm watch means that thunderstorms may occur as the weather conditions are right to produce thunderstorms. A thunderstorm warning means that a thunderstorm is occurring at that time. When a watch is issued, people should be prepared in the event that the weather event does occur and should be paying attention to changing weather conditions. When a warning is issued, people should act immediately to protect themselves from the weather event.

Lab 11

The Solar System

Measuring Distance in Space

There are three main units of measure when determining the distance between objects in space. They are the astronomical unit, the light year, and the parsec.

The astronomical unit (AU) is the average distance between the Earth and the Sun which is approximately 150 million kilometers or 93 million miles. This unit of measure works well within our solar system but is not ideal for measuring larger distances.

The light year is the distance light travels in one Earth year. Light travels at approximately 300,000 kilometers per second (186,000 miles per second). Therefore, a light year is about 9.5 trillion kilometers or 6 trillion miles. One light year is 63,241 astronomical units.

A parsec is 3.26 light years. That is roughly 31 trillion kilometers (just over 19 trillion miles) or 206,264 astronomical units.

The Sun

The Sun appears to have been active for 4.6 billion years and has enough fuel to go on for another five billion years or so. When compared to other stars in our galaxy, the Sun is considered 'average,' but it is still our primary source of energy and is studied by astronomers since it is the only star whose surface features can be observed in detail. The Sun rotates differentially, meaning it takes fewer days to complete one rotation near its equator than near its poles. This unequal period of rotation causes variations in the Sun's magnetic field, which in turn influences many surface features. Internal nuclear fusion reactions cause four protons (hydrogen nuclei) to fuse together to form one alpha particle (helium nucleus). The alpha particle is about 0.7% less massive than the four protons and the difference is expelled as energy and carried to the surface of the Sun where the energy is released as light and heat. Energy from the core takes a million years to reach the surface. This process of losing mass means the Sun is becoming lighter as time goes on.

Some features of the Sun are seen in the image below from NASA (fig. 11.1). The Sun's outer visible layer is called the photosphere and has a temperature of 6,000°C (11,000°F). This layer has a mottled appearance due to the turbulent eruptions of energy at the surface. The chromosphere is above the photosphere. Solar energy passes through this region on its way out from the center of the

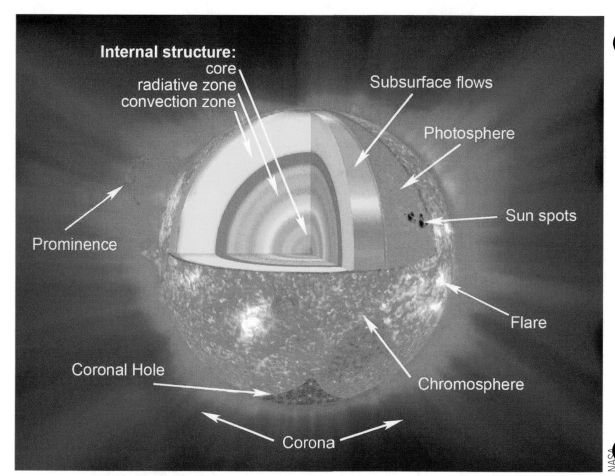

Figure 11.1 Features of our Sun

Sun. Granules are small (about 1000 km across) cellular features that cover the entire Sun except for areas covered by sunspots. Granules are the tops of convection cells where hot fluid rises up from the interior in the bright areas, spreads out across the surface, cools, and then sinks inward along the dark lanes. Flares are bright filaments of hot gas emerging from sunspot regions. The corona is the outer part of the Sun's atmosphere which is only visible during a total solar eclipse. It is in this region that prominences appear. Prominences are immense clouds of glowing gas that erupt from the upper chromosphere. The solar wind streams off of the Sun in all directions at speeds of about 400 km/s (about 1 million miles per hour). The source of the solar wind is the Sun's hot corona. The fluctuations in radiation given off by the Sun, such as with sun spot cycles and solar flares are thought to have an effect on Earth's climate.

The Sun is the richest source of electromagnetic energy and contains the majority of the mass in our solar system (about 99.86%). The Sun's nearest known stellar neighbor is a red dwarf star Proxima Centauri, at a distance of 4.2 light years away.

The Moon

Located at an average distance of 384,401 km (238,239 miles), the Moon is the nearest celestial neighbor to the Earth. The Moon is a natural satellite and has a monthly counter-clockwise revolution around the Earth. The phases viewed by observers on Earth are associated with the Earth-Moon revolution around the Sun. The Moon's position relative to the Sun produces the phases observed. As the Moon moves in its orbit, its slow counter-clockwise rotation results in the same side continuously facing the Earth. The Moon has no atmosphere, and therefore no land forms are produced from wind or water erosion. The majority of lunar surface features are the result of ancient volcanic eruptions and impact craters from meteorites and further modified by bombardment of micrometeorites.

Phases of the Moon

The lunar phases observed from Earth are the result of the motion of the moon and sunlight that is reflected from the Moon's surface. The half of the Moon facing directly toward the Sun is illuminated at all times. However, to an observer on Earth, the percentage of the bright side that is visible depends on the location of the Moon with respect to the Sun and Earth. When the Moon lies between the Sun and Earth, none of the bright side can be seen. This phase is called the 'new moon.' Conversely, when the Moon is located on the opposite side of the Earth from the Sun, all of its bright side is visible, producing a 'full moon.' Only a fraction of the illuminated half is visible during any position between these extremes. Notice on the image of Moon phases provided by NASA (fig. 11.2) that the illuminated half of the Moon is always directly toward the Sun.

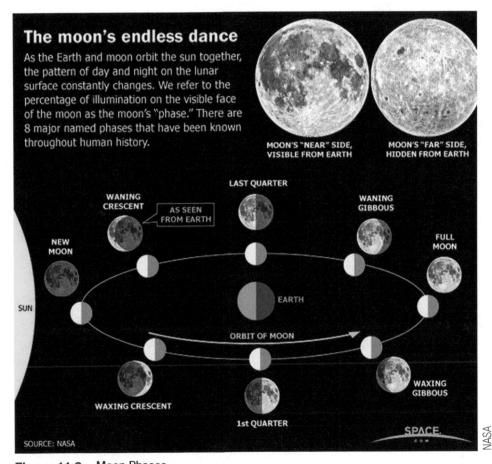

Figure 11.2   Moon Phases

Eclipses

Eclipses occur when the Sun, Moon, and Earth are in a direct line. A lunar eclipse occurs when the Moon falls within the Earth's shadow. A lunar eclipse can occur only at a full Moon. There are three types: total, partial, and penumbral. A total lunar eclipse occurs when the Sun, Earth, and Moon are perfectly lined up. Anything less than perfect creates a partial or no eclipse at all. Because the Moon's orbit around Earth lies in a slightly different plane than Earth's orbit around the Sun, perfect alignment for an eclipse does not occur every full Moon. Penumbral lunar eclipse occurs when the Moon is in Earth's faint outer, or penumbral, shadow. This effect is not typically noticed.

A solar eclipse is when the Moon moves in a line directly between the Earth and the Sun. The Moon casts a shadow over the Earth. A solar eclipse can only take place during the phase of a new Moon. There are three types of solar eclipses: Total, partial, and annular. A total eclipse occurs when the orbital planes intersect and the distances align favorably, a new Moon can appear to completely blot out the disk of the Sun. A partial eclipse occurs when only the penumbra (partial shadow) passes in front of part of the Sun. This partial eclipse can vary depending on the viewer's position to the path of the eclipse. An annular solar eclipse is similar to a total eclipse, only the elliptical orbit creates a distance where the Moon's shadow is not enough to extend out to completely block the Sun. Therefore, the Moon appears to pass centrally across the Sun, but it is too small to cover the disk of the Sun completely.

Lunar Features

The surface of the Moon can be classified as one of two types: terrae (which is plural of the Latin word terra for 'land') or maria (which is the plural of the Latin word mare for 'sea'). Terrae are lunar highlands, which are the bright areas of the Moon seen from Earth. Maria are flat, lowland regions creating the dark features. Together these features create the 'face on the moon.' Craters are the most obvious features on the surface produced when rapidly moving debris impacts the lunar surface. Look at the images of the surface of the Moon below (fig. 11.3) and notice the numerous features in the terra and mare. Other features include linear rilles, mare ridges, and crater chains (impact craters in a row).

Rotation and Revolution of Planets

Rotation is the turning of a planet about its axis. This is responsible for day and night. When the solar system is viewed from above the Northern hemisphere of Earth, the planets (except Venus) rotate in a counterclockwise direction. Venus on the other hand rotates very slowly to in a clockwise direction. The time it takes for a planet to rotate 360° on its axis is called the period of rotation. The motion of a planet around the Sun is called revolution. The length of time it takes for a planet to make a complete revolution around the Sun it that planet's year and is called the period of revolution. When viewed from above the Northern hemisphere of the Earth, the revolution of all planets around the Sun is counterclockwise.

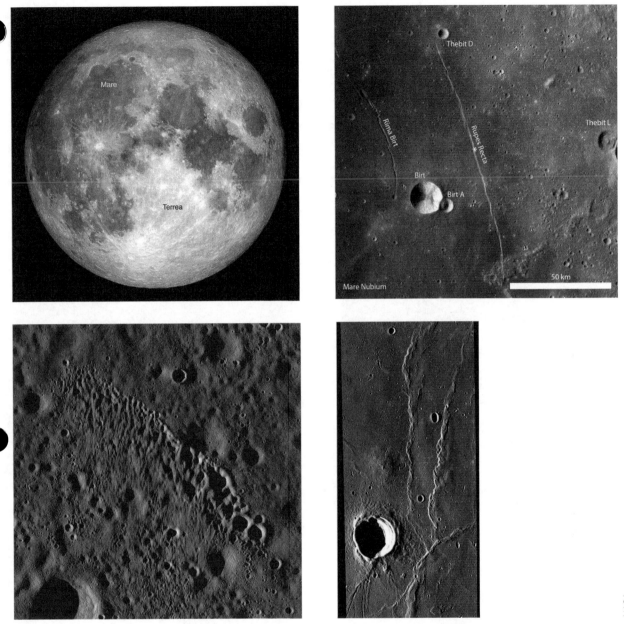

Figure 11.3 Lunar mare are the darker areas of the Moon and terrae are the lighter areas. Lunar rilles, crater chains, and mare ridges are common features on the Moon's surface

NASA

The Planet Controversy

Recently there has been a great deal of debate about the status of Pluto. Is it or is it not a planet? As of June, 2008, Pluto has been reclassified as a special type of dwarf planet called a plutoid. So the question becomes: What is a planet? According the International Astronomical Union (IAU), these are the current definitions used to determine what is and is not a planet.

A **planet** is a celestial body that:

　a. is in orbit around the Sun

　b. has sufficient mass for its self-gravity to overcome rigid body forces so that it assumes a hydrostatic equilibrium (nearly spherical) shape

　c. has cleared the neighborhood around its orbit.

A **dwarf planet** is a celestial body that:

　a. is in orbit around the Sun

　b. has sufficient mass for its self-gravity to overcome rigid body forces so that it assumes a hydrostatic equilibrium (nearly spherical) shape

　c. has not cleared the neighborhood around its orbit

　d. is not a satellite

A **plutoid** is a special dwarf planet that:

　a. is in orbit around the Sun

　b. has sufficient mass for its self-gravity to overcome rigid body forces so that it assumes a hydrostatic equilibrium (nearly spherical) shape

　c. has not cleared the neighborhood around its orbit

　d. is not a satellite

　e. has a semi-major axis greater than that of Neptune

　f. must have a minimum brightness

All other bodies, except satellites, are called "small solar system bodies."

Our Solar System

Our solar system (fig. 11.4) contains objects ranging in size from the Sun to tiny grains of rock in the asteroid belt. For thousands of years man has gazed from Earth to the vast expanse of cosmic ocean of our solar system which is made up of eight planets, multiple dwarf planets, more than 170 moons, as well as dust, gas, and thousands of asteroids and comets, all orbiting around the Sun. The inner solar system is from the Sun to Mars and includes asteroids, satellites, and space junk. The outer solar system is Jupiter to Eris including comets asteroids and dwarf planets. Scientists believe there may be hundreds or thousands of dwarf planets awaiting discovery.

The Terrestrial Planets

Mercury (fig. 11.5) has a diameter of about 4,900 km (3,000 miles) and, on average, is 58 million km (36 million miles) from the Sun. One day on Mercury is about 176 Earth days and Mercury's year is about 88 Earth days. Because of its small size, it has no atmosphere. With no atmosphere,

Figure 11.4 The major objects of our solar system

Figure 11.5 NASA image of the Sun's closest planet Mercury. Note the large number of craters on the surface

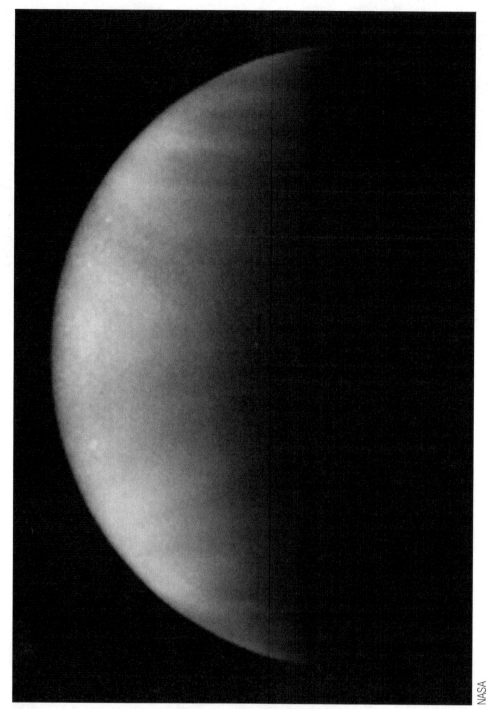

NASA

Figure 11.6   The cloud tops of Venus as photographed by the Hubble Space Telescope

impact craters are common because there is nothing to burn them up or slow them. The core of Mercury consumes about 80% of the planet. The average daily temperature on Mercury ranges from -180 to 430°C. Mercury has no moons and has an equatorial inclination of 0°.

Venus (fig. 11.6) is much closer to the size of the Earth with a diameter of 12,100 km (7,500 miles) and is approximately 108 million km (67 million miles) from the Sun. One day on Venus is equal to 255 Earth days, and one year on Venus is 243 Earth days. The atmosphere is very thick and contains mostly CO_2 and sulfuric acid. The atmosphere causes a runaway greenhouse effect which keeps the temperature around 462°C. The former Soviet Union landed two space craft on Venus and the United States landed one in the late 1970s. The spacecraft survived long enough to send a few images back to Earth before melting due to the atmospheric conditions. Venus also has no moons. Unlike the other planets, Venus rotates clockwise on the rotational axis. The equatorial inclination of Venus is 177.3° due to its retrograde rotation.

Earth has a diameter of 12,750 km (7,921 miles) and orbits the Sun at a distance of approximately 150 million km (93 million miles). Earth is tilted from the equatorial plane at 23.5°. It has a solid nickel & iron inner core surrounded by a molten outer core. The mantle comprises the bulk of the planet and varies from solid to semi-molten. Earth has one Moon. Earth's Moon has a diameter of 3,500 km (2,174 miles). The current theory is that the Moon was created from debris ejected from Earth after a collision with a body about the size of Mars. This debris field coalesced into the Moon after that. While there is some evidence of volcanic activity on the Moon, it apparently ceased shortly after the Moon formed. The composition of rocks returned to Earth by the Apollo missions indicate the Moon has high concentrations of iron, nickel, and magnesium which is very similar to basaltic rocks on Earth.

Mars is the last of the terrestrial planets (fig. 11.7). It has a diameter of 6,800 km (4,200 miles) and is approximately 228 million km (142 million miles) from the Sun. A day on Mars is slightly

Figure 11.7   The surface of Mars from the Curiosity rover

longer than a day on Earth (24.62 hours) and takes 687 Earth days to revolve around the Sun. While Mars may have had a thick atmosphere in the past, current theory states that most of the atmosphere was lost to space after an impact with a large meteor or the solar wind blew the atmosphere away due to the low gravity of Mars. The current atmosphere is very thin and composed mostly of CO_2. Recent exploration has provided considerable evidence that liquid water flowed on Mars in the past and satellite images have shown evidence of recent water flow. Mars has two small moons named Phobos and Deimos which may be captured asteroids and is also home to the largest known volcano in the solar system (Olympus Mons). The temperature on Mars ranges from -153 to 20°C and Mars is inclined at 25.2°.

The asteroid belt lies between Mars and Jupiter. This area should contain another planet and much debate surrounds the origin of the asteroid belt. One theory is that a planet did form but was later destroyed by an impact with another space body. A competing theory states that a planet tried to form but failed due to the gravitational pull of Jupiter that prevented the fragments from coalescing into a planet. Jupiter's gravity does upset the orbit of asteroids at times causing them to spiral toward the Sun where they could pose a danger to Earth. Vesta (fig. 11.8) is the largest of the asteroids and is about 530 km in diameter.

The Jovian Planets

Jupiter (fig. 11.9) is the largest planet in the solar system with a diameter of approximately 140,000 km (86,800 miles) and orbits the Sun at a distance of 778 million km (484 million miles). A day on Jupiter is about 10 hours and one revolution takes about 4,333 Earth days (12 years). Jupiter may have a rocky core about the size of Earth and is surrounded by a metallic gaseous mixture primarily comprised of hydrogen and helium. Jupiter has 67 known objects in its orbit and has a faint ring system. The average temperature on Jupiter is about -148°C and Jupiter is inclined at 3.1°. The

Figure 11.8   Vesta is the largest of the asteroids but many are as small as 10m in diameter

Great Red Spot on Jupiter is a very large storm system which is about the size of Earth. The storm has been observed for over 350 years.

The second gas giant is Saturn (fig. 11.10). Saturn has a diameter of approximately 120,000 km (75,000 miles) and is approximately 1.4 billion km (886 million miles) from the Sun. A day on

Figure 11.9 The gas giant Jupiter with the Great Red Spot and the moon Io

Figure 11.10 Saturn and the spectacular ring system

Saturn is about 10.7 Earth hours and a single revolution around the Sun takes about 10,756 Earth days (29 years). Its core is surrounded by a metallic hydrogen shell, but near the surface the planet is comprised of a mixture of liquid hydrogen and helium. Average daily temperature on Saturn is approximately -178°C. Saturn has 62 known objects in orbit and has a ring system comprised of 7 individual rings. The equatorial inclination of Saturn is 26.7°.

Uranus is unique because its spin axis is tilted at 97.8° from vertical (fig. 11.11). The reason is unknown, but could be the result of a large impactor knocking Uranus on its side. The magnetic field is also about 60° from vertical. The diameter of Uranus is approximately 51,100km (31,700 miles) and orbits the Sun at a distance of 2.9 billion km (1.8 billion miles). One rotation takes 17 Earth hours while one revolution is about 30,687 Earth days (84 Earth years). The average temperature is -216°C, and the atmosphere is mostly hydrogen, helium, and methane. Uranus has 27 known satellites and possesses rings like Saturn. Like Venus, Uranus rotates clockwise.

The final planet in our solar system is Neptune (fig. 11.12). With a diameter of 49,500 km (30,750 miles), Neptune is the smallest of the gas giants. Neptune orbits the Sun at a distance of 4.5 billion km (2.8 billion miles) and rotates on its axis in 16 Earth hours but requires 60,190 Earth days (165 Earth years) to revolve around the Sun. While the core appears to be very similar to that of Earth, the remainder of the planet is composed of water, ammonia (NH_3), and methane (CH_4) and the atmosphere is comprised of hydrogen, helium, and methane ice which gives Neptune its unique deep blue color. Neptune has 6 rings and 13 known satellites. The average temperature is −214°C. The magnetic field of Neptune is tilted 47° from vertical, and Neptune is inclined at 28.3°.

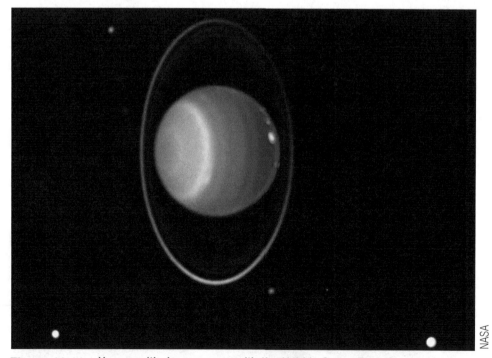

Figure 11.11   Uranus with rings as seen with the Hubble Space Telescope

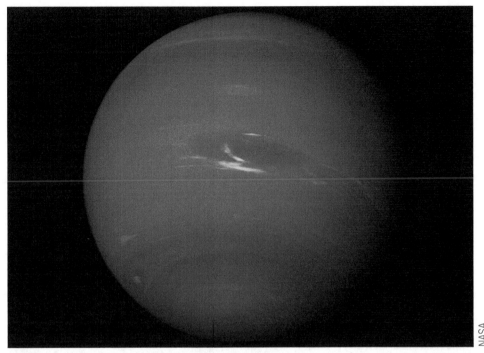

Figure 11.12   The last of the gas giants planets, Neptune

Dwarf Planets and Plutoids

Ceres (fig. 11.13) is located in the asteroid belt between Mars and Jupiter and is the smallest of the dwarf planets with a diameter of approximately 932 km (592 miles). Ceres is the largest object in the asteroid belt and comprises about 25% of the volume of the asteroid belt. The diameter of Ceres makes it about as wide as the state of Texas. The surface is probably covered with water ice along with hydrated carbonates and clay and appears to be differentiated into a rocky core with an ice mantle; therefore, Ceres has a structure similar to the terrestrial planets but is much more dense. Ceres has a mean temperature of −122°C and an orbital period of 4.6 years with a day of 9 Earth hours.

Pluto is smaller than Earth's Moon with a diameter of 2,300 km (1,030 miles), about half the width of the United States (fig. 11.14). Pluto orbits at an average of 5.9 billion km (3.7 billion miles) from the Sun. At times its orbit is beyond Neptune, but for long periods it is closer to the Sun than Neptune. On its close passes to the Sun, the surface may melt enough to produce some weather systems and remove evidence of impacts from other bodies before it refreezes. It may have a small, rocky core surrounded by water ice with a surface covering of frozen methane, nitrogen, and carbon dioxide. Pluto has five known satellites with four of them (Nix, Hydra, Styx, and Kerberos) being less than 160 km in diameter. Charon is the largest satellite of Pluto with a diameter about half that of Pluto (fig. 11.15). Pluto has a daily temperature of −233 to −223°C. Pluto has an eccentric orbit around the Sun and takes 248 years for one revolution and has a rotational period of 6.5 Earth days. NASA still classifies Pluto as a planet. The International Astronomical Union (IAU) classifies Pluto as a plutoid.

Eris is larger than Pluto with a diameter of 2,500 km (1,552.5 miles) and was discovered in 2003. It may have a methane ice covered surface similar to Pluto. Eris has one known satellite named

NASA

Figure 11.13   The dwarf planet Ceres is the largest object in the asteroid belt but the smallest of the dwarf planets

NASA

Figure 11.14   The dwarf planet Pluto was discovered in 1930

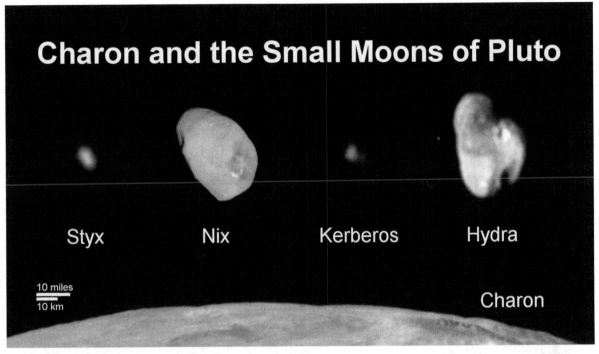

Figure 11.15   The satellites of Pluto

Dysnomia and a daily temperature of −243 to −217°C. Like Pluto, its orbit around the Sun is eccentric with an orbital period of 557 Earth years because Eris is about 10.2 billion km from the Sun. The methane ice on its surface may sublimate at Eris' closest approach to the Sun.

Quaoar was discovered in 2002 and has a diameter of about 1,300 km and has one moon. The orbit of Quaoar is about 6 billion km from the Sun with a revolution period of about 289 Earth years. As with other plutoids, Quaoar is probably ice covered with some methane.

Haumea was discovered in 2003 and rotates on its axis in about 4 hours making it one of the fastest rotating objects known. Haumea is about the same size as Pluto but the rapid rotation has stretched it into a slightly elongated shape. Haumea has 2 known satellites and orbits at a distance of about 6.4 billion km.

Makemake was discovered in 2005. It has a diameter of approximately 1,500 km (931.5 miles). Its surface is probably covered in a mixture of methane and nitrogen ice and has a daily temperature of −244 to −249°C. There are no known satellites of Makemake at this time. Like the other plutoids, Makemake has an eccentric orbit with an orbital period of 310 years and orbits the Sun at approximately 6.8 billion km. Some of the ice on the surface may melt during Makemake's closest approach to the Sun creating an atmosphere.

Other Solar System Bodies

Comets are basically balls of ice, dust, and rock. They may contain a small rocky core. As a comet approaches the Sun, the outer surface heats causing the ice to melt which releases gases which form a coma. As this material is blown off of the comet by the solar wind, it forms the tail.

Figure 11.16   The currently known and largest of the objects past Neptune with Earth for comparison

The Kuiper Belt (fig. 11.17) extends from Neptune (30AU) to a distance of 50 AU. It contains thousands of small icy bodies, some of which are large or larger than Pluto. This is part of the reason Pluto was downgraded to a dwarf planet (now a special dwarf planet called a plutoid). These bodies circle the Sun with extremely long period orbits (hundreds to thousands of years). Pluto's orbit takes it into the Kuiper Belt at its furthest point from the Sun.

Beyond the Kuiper Belt is the Oort Cloud (fig. 11.17) which extends from 50 AU to the edge of the Sun's gravitational influence. This is an area of billions of small, icy bodies slowly orbiting the Sun. Because of the gravitational field of some of the outer planets, their orbit is occasionally disturbed causing one of them to approach the Sun producing a very long period comet.

Sedna (fig. 11.16) was the first Oort Cloud object discovered and is believed to be about 1,280km in diameter. At the farthest point of Sedna's orbit it is about 130 billion km from the Sun and has an orbital period of 10,500 Earth years.

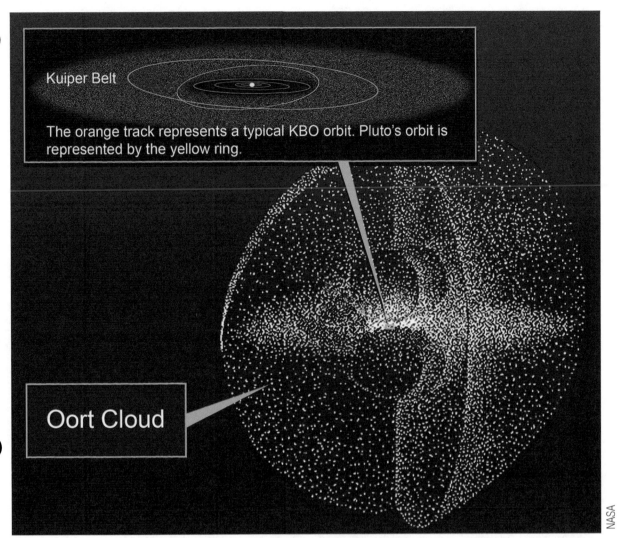

Figure 11.17 The Kuiper Belt extends from Neptune to a distance of 50AU. Pluto's orbit takes it into the Kuiper Belt. The Oort Cloud begins at 50AU and extends to the limit of the Sun's gravitational influence

Lab 12

Galaxies and the Universe

Solar System vs Galaxy vs Universe

Solar systems are the smallest of the three systems in question. A solar system consists of a star and the objects affected by its gravity. These objects include planets, moons, asteroids, comets, and meteoroids.

A galaxy is a system of solar systems and other stars. Galaxies, like solar systems, are held together by gravity. In galaxies, large systems of stars held together by mutual gravitation and isolated from similar systems by vast regions of space. The galaxy that contains the Earth and its solar system is called the Milky Way Galaxy. The Milky Way measures about 100,000 light-years across, and is thought to contain 200 billion stars. Solar systems orbit around their galaxies just as planets orbit around their stars. It takes the Earth's solar system roughly 200 to 250 million years to complete its orbit.

The universe is the largest of the three astronomical ideas being compared. All things, including galaxies and solar systems, are included within the realm of the universe. The universe is the totality of known or supposed objects and phenomena throughout space, the cosmos, macrocosm.

- We live on planet Earth which is part of our local Solar System.

- Our Solar System includes the Sun and everything that orbits the Sun.

- Our Sun is just one star in the Milky Way Galaxy.

- The Milky Way Galaxy is just one galaxy in the Universe.

The Formation of the Universe

The Big Bang Theory says that all matter was a mass of free protons, neutrons, and electrons which could not combine together because of tremendous temperature and pressure. This matter would have occupied a space between the Earth and Sun. An explosion scattered these particles and propelled them outward. As cooling occurred, the protons, neutrons, and electrons could finally combine to form atoms. These condensed into gases and heavier elements and finally into galactic systems. The Big Bang Theory says stars are radiating away from a center and will disperse to the furthest part of the universe. All possible stages in the origin of the universe are present and visible today because the universe is undergoing constant growth and evolutionary change.

The Steady State Theory postulates that the density of matter in the universe remains unchanged as new matter is created between galaxies as the universe expands. Therefore, the observed universe is the same as it has always been. The rate of creation of new matter is at the same rate that older galaxies recede. This allows the universe to remain filled with matter at uniform density.

The Oscillating Universe Theory was developed in 1934. This theory says that for every Big Bang there is a Big Crunch. The universe starts with a Big Bang and matter is dispersed radially outward from a starting point just as in the Big Bang Theory. After initial expansion, gravitational pull between particles prevails as energy dwindles. This pulls the particles back toward each other and the original center until the material is compressed to the point that molecules break down into their individual components (protons, neutrons, and electrons). This is a result of increasing temperature and pressure as the particles are compressed. Therefore, the system becomes a pulsating or oscillating one. This theory would mean that the universe is created and destroyed over and over again on a cycle of about 80–100 billion years.

The Origin of the Solar System

The best current theory to explain the origin of our solar system is the Solar Nebula Hypothesis. The solar system began with a cold, diffuse cloud of gas and dust particles. These particles were being pushed around by the pressure of light which caused the cloud to contract, flatten, and begin to rotate. In time, as much as 90% of the material would concentrate in the middle of the cloud. As the mass began to spin turbulent flow would cause eddies to form where matter would accumulate. A balance was reached between the centrifugal force of the swirling mass and gravity which would allow masses to form as the cloud shrank. The planets would have begun to form due to accretion. This random process caused the planets to be homogeneous. Over long periods of time, protoplanets formed which were much larger than the planets currently are. The gravitational pull and large mass of material in the center would have condensed as gravity increased causing the temperature to rise to several million degrees C. Spontaneous fusion would occur creating a new star. As this star (the Sun) continued to heat and produce a magnetic field, matter would have been pulled from the surrounding nebula which slowed the rotation. Solar wind blew matter away from the Sun removing many of the lighter elements from the inner protoplanets, leading to the formation of the terrestrial planets. The lighter material would have accumulated around the outer planets forming the Jovian planets. The planets would have started to condense due to gravity and their internal heat would have increased. The increased heat and radioactivity eventually caused the terrestrial planets to differentiate into the layered bodies we now know.

Bode's Law

The Titius-Bode Law (often referred to as Bode's Law) is rough rule that predicts the spacing of the planets in the solar system. The law relates the mean distances of the planets from the Sun to a simple mathematical progression of numbers. This calculation gives a sequence of numbers that

Table 12.1 Bode's law accurately predicts the distance from the Sun to each planet

Planetary body	Distance from Sun (AU)	Predicted distance
Mercury	0.39	0.40
Venus	0.72	0.70
Earth	1.00	1.00
Mars	1.52	1.60
Asteroid Belt	2.80	2.80
Jupiter	5.20	5.20
Saturn	9.54	10.00
Uranus	19.19	19.60
Neptune	30.07	38.80

represent the distance from the Sun to each planet. The formula, $D = (n+4)/10$ (where $n = 0, 3, 6, 12, 24, 48, 96, . . .$), very accurately estimates the distance (in astronomical units) from the Sun to each planet and predicts the location of a planet between Mars and Jupiter (Table 12.1). This law can also be used to calculate the distance for moons around planets.

How do we locate exoplanets and what should we look for?

There are several methods used to detect exoplanets in orbits around stars. Because of the immense distances between the Earth and other stars, direct observation of exoplanets is not possible. However, using the following methods, we can still learn a great deal about exoplanets.

Radial Velocity or Doppler Spectroscopy

The most successful (to date) method of locating exoplanets is the radial velocity or Doppler Spectroscopy method. The radial velocity method uses shifts in the spectrum of light emitted from a star to determine if an exoplanet is orbiting the star. As an exoplanet orbits its host star, the position of the star changes moving slightly toward or away from the Earth. If the star moves toward Earth, the light it emits is shifted toward the blue end of the spectrum and the light shifts toward the red end of the spectrum when the star moves away from Earth. This change in the light spectrum is monitored by telescopes to determine if the change occurs on a regular, repeating basis at the same interval that indicates the presence of an object orbiting a star. The radial velocity method cannot accurately determine the mass of an object but can be used to determine the minimum mass of an orbiting object. Therefore, instead of a planet, there could be another small star in orbit around the star being observed. This method is more effective at locating large exoplanets than small ones.

Transit Photometry

As a planet orbits around a star when the planet passes in front of the star, that is called a transit. The transit will block part of the light from the star causing a slight dimming of the star thus allowing astronomers to use the transit photometry method for detecting exoplanets (fig. 12.1). The

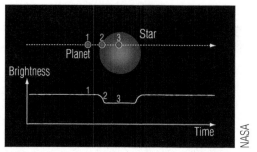

Figure 12.1 A simple graph showing how the light from a star would dim due to the transit of an exoplanet

slight dimming that is observed provides an estimate of the size of the object orbiting the star. Large exoplanets will block more of the star's light than a small exoplanet. Using this method and radial velocity, the density of the exoplanet can be determined which provides an excellent idea about the composition of the exoplanet (is it a gas giant like Jupiter or a rocky world like Earth).

By observing the light spectrum of the star when the planet is hidden then comparing that spectrum to the observed spectrum when the exoplanet is transiting the star, the composition of the atmosphere of the exoplanet can be determined. This can be done because the light from the star will be partially absorbed by the atmosphere of the planet causing the wavelength of certain light from the star to not be observed on Earth. Because certain elements absorb certain wavelengths of light, we can then know what the composition of the exoplanet's atmosphere is.

Mircolensing

Using microlensing, exoplanets from very distant stars can be detected. This method depends on another star (the lens star) being in the path of the light between Earth and a star that is being observed (the source star). When the light from the source star passes by the lens star, the gravity of the lens star causes the light from the source star to bend making it appear the two stars are further away from each other than normal. If the lens star is directly in the path of the light from the source star, Earth-based telescopes cannot differentiate between the two stars so it will make it appear we are seeing one much brighter star. This effect can also make it appear that the source star is in two locations (fig. 12.2).

If another body is orbiting the lens star, the gravity of that body will also bend the light from the source star. This may make it appear that there are three of the source stars. This will also make it appear that the light from the source star has become much brighter. The microlensing effect may last several hours to several days and will not be repeated unless the lens and source star align themselves properly again.

Goldilocks Zone (Habitable Zone)

Earth has been called the "Goldilocks planet." In the story of "Goldilocks and the Three Bears," a little girl named Goldilocks liked everything just right. On Earth, everything is just right for life as we know it to exist. It is warm, but not too warm and it has liquid water, but not too much water. This

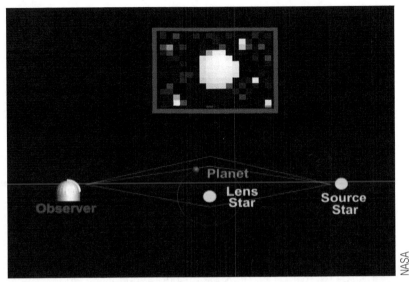

Figure 12.2   Microlensing can be used to find exoplanets at much greater distances than the other current methods

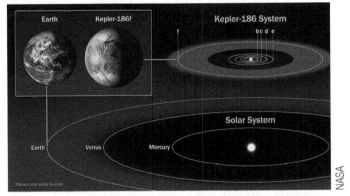

Figure 12.3   This image compares the habitable zone of our solar system to the Kepler-186 solar system. The exoplanet Kepler-186f was the first Earth size planet located in the habitable zone of another star

'ideal' zone is called the Habitable Zone or Goldilocks Zone (fig. 12.3) and specifies the relationship between planets and the host star needed to maintain liquid water and a proper temperature (too close and it's too hot, too far away, and it's a frigid ice planet). Scientists are continuously searching for possible 'Earth-like' planets and have discovered some possibilities. The idea is not necessarily to find an exact match, but a close one. For example, astronomers have discovered several so-called "super-Earths" (planets that are slightly larger than our home).

Black Holes

A black hole (fig. 12.4) is anything but empty space. Rather, it is a great amount of matter packed into a very small area – think of a star 10 times more massive than the Sun squeezed into a sphere approximately the diameter of New York City. The result is a gravitational field so strong that nothing, not even light, can escape.

NASA

Figure 12.4 An image of the black hole in the middle of the spiral galaxy M81 taken by the Chandra X-ray Observatory

Black holes were predicted by Einstein's theory of general relativity, which showed that when a massive star dies, it leaves behind a small, dense remnant core. If the core's mass is more than about three times the mass of the Sun, the equations showed that the force of gravity overwhelms all other forces and produces a black hole.

Black holes pull matter and even energy into themselves – but no more so than other stars or cosmic objects of similar mass. That means that a black hole with the mass of our own Sun would not 'suck' objects into it any more than our own Sun does with its own gravitational pull.

Planets, light, and other matter must pass close to a black hole in order to be pulled into its grasp. When they reach a point of no return they are said to have entered the event horizon – the point from which any escape is impossible because it requires moving faster than the speed of light.

It is believed black holes exist on two radically different size scales. On the one end, there are the countless black holes that are the remnants of massive stars. Peppered throughout the Universe, these 'stellar mass' black holes are generally 10–24 times as massive as the Sun. Most stellar black holes lead isolated lives and are impossible to detect. Judging from the number of stars large enough to produce such black holes, however, scientists estimate that there are as many as ten million to a billion such black holes in the Milky Way alone. On the other end of the size spectrum are the giants known as "supermassive" black holes, which are millions, if not billions, of times as massive as the Sun. Astronomers believe that supermassive black holes lie at the center of virtually all large galaxies, even our own Milky Way. Astronomers can detect them by watching for their effects on nearby stars and gas.

Constellations

Asterism is a word for a pattern of stars in the sky which appears to be so distinctive that it is easily identifiable and remembered. In ancient times, people saw asterisms and made up stories about mythological creatures and characters which they associated with the star patterns. As astronomers subsequently began to make maps of the stars, the named asterisms were included in the maps and called constellations.

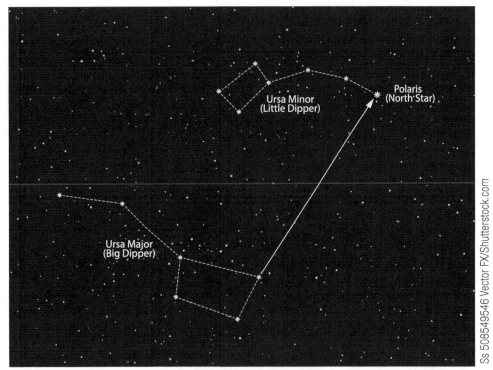

Ss 508549546 Vector FX/Shutterstock.com

Figure 12.5 If you project Earth's rotational axis out of the North Pole into space it will always point to Polaris. The two stars that make up the cup of Ursa Major (the Big Dipper) can be followed to locate Polaris which is at the end of the handle of Ursa Minor (the Little Dipper)

As time passed, the sky became filled with constellations, many of which included the same stars. In 1925 the International Astronomical Union stepped in to gain control and make sense of things. They adopted 88 official constellations and assigned areas of the sky to specific constellation names.

There are some asterisms which are not official constellations but are located within one or more constellations. One you are probably familiar with is the Big Dipper, which actually makes up the bear's tail and flank of the constellation Ursa Major. Consider other recognizable features in the night sky which have been used for navigation for thousands of years, such as Polaris (or what you might call the North Star). Polaris (fig. 12.5) is part of the constellation Ursa Minor (the tip of the tail), and is more commonly noticed as the end of the Little Dipper handle. Polaris is very distant from Earth (about 390 light years; almost 25 million AU) and is in an ideal position for marking North because of its position in relation to Earth's axis.

At different times of year, different constellations can be seen in the sky. Constellations shift gradually to the west through the year as Earth orbits the Sun. Different constellations can also be seen depending on where you are on Earth. There are also features you will not be able to see from certain locations because of the spherical shape of Earth.